MW00630458

A) Simplify the fractions.

1) $\frac{35}{56}$ = ______ 2) $\frac{8}{24}$ = ______ 3) $\frac{21}{56}$ = ______ 4) $\frac{9}{36}$ = ______

5) $\frac{2}{10}$ = ______ 6) $\frac{14}{42}$ = ______ 7) $\frac{16}{20}$ = ______ 8) $\frac{6}{8}$ = ______

9) $\frac{9}{72}$ = ______ 10) $\frac{15}{30}$ = ______ 11) $\frac{4}{6}$ = ______ 12) $\frac{63}{72}$ = ______

13) $\frac{21}{35}$ = ______ 14) $\frac{12}{18}$ = ______ 15) $\frac{4}{24}$ = ______ 16) $\frac{14}{21}$ = ______

17) $\frac{4}{12}$ = ______ 18) $\frac{20}{40}$ = ______ 19) $\frac{12}{15}$ = ______ 20) $\frac{14}{28}$ = ______

21) $\frac{27}{45}$ = ______ 22) $\frac{3}{9}$ = ______ 23) $\frac{9}{54}$ = ______ 24) $\frac{2}{8}$ = ______

25) $\frac{2}{16}$ = ______ 26) $\frac{3}{24}$ = ______ 27) $\frac{3}{18}$ = ______ 28) $\frac{20}{25}$ = ______

29) $\frac{5}{15}$ = ______ 30) $\frac{6}{24}$ = ______ 31) $\frac{8}{16}$ = ______ 32) $\frac{18}{24}$ = ______

B) Simplify the fractions.

1) $\frac{3}{15}$ = ________ 2) $\frac{9}{12}$ = ________ 3) $\frac{10}{25}$ = ________ 4) $\frac{12}{32}$ = ________

5) $\frac{9}{54}$ = ________ 6) $\frac{6}{24}$ = ________ 7) $\frac{8}{12}$ = ________ 8) $\frac{18}{27}$ = ________

9) $\frac{18}{36}$ = ________ 10) $\frac{16}{40}$ = ________ 11) $\frac{4}{16}$ = ________ 12) $\frac{15}{30}$ = ________

13) $\frac{3}{24}$ = ________ 14) $\frac{4}{12}$ = ________ 15) $\frac{8}{16}$ = ________ 16) $\frac{24}{36}$ = ________

17) $\frac{5}{15}$ = ________ 18) $\frac{6}{36}$ = ________ 19) $\frac{14}{35}$ = ________ 20) $\frac{5}{20}$ = ________

21) $\frac{20}{32}$ = ________ 22) $\frac{6}{16}$ = ________ 23) $\frac{3}{12}$ = ________ 24) $\frac{27}{72}$ = ________

25) $\frac{10}{15}$ = ________ 26) $\frac{32}{40}$ = ________ 27) $\frac{10}{30}$ = ________ 28) $\frac{6}{18}$ = ________

29) $\frac{12}{16}$ = ________ 30) $\frac{18}{30}$ = ________ 31) $\frac{27}{45}$ = ________ 32) $\frac{9}{24}$ = ________

C) Simplify the fractions.

1) $\frac{30}{40}$ = ________ 2) $\frac{16}{24}$ = ________ 3) $\frac{9}{12}$ = ________ 4) $\frac{4}{12}$ = ________

5) $\frac{27}{45}$ = ________ 6) $\frac{24}{36}$ = ________ 7) $\frac{2}{16}$ = ________ 8) $\frac{2}{8}$ = ________

9) $\frac{8}{24}$ = ________ 10) $\frac{18}{24}$ = ________ 11) $\frac{40}{64}$ = ________ 12) $\frac{9}{18}$ = ________

13) $\frac{16}{40}$ = ________ 14) $\frac{9}{27}$ = ________ 15) $\frac{6}{8}$ = ________ 16) $\frac{16}{32}$ = ________

17) $\frac{9}{54}$ = ________ 18) $\frac{24}{40}$ = ________ 19) $\frac{12}{24}$ = ________ 20) $\frac{9}{15}$ = ________

21) $\frac{21}{24}$ = ________ 22) $\frac{8}{40}$ = ________ 23) $\frac{24}{64}$ = ________ 24) $\frac{9}{36}$ = ________

25) $\frac{2}{6}$ = ________ 26) $\frac{40}{48}$ = ________ 27) $\frac{4}{10}$ = ________ 28) $\frac{12}{18}$ = ________

29) $\frac{18}{48}$ = ________ 30) $\frac{8}{16}$ = ________ 31) $\frac{4}{6}$ = ________ 32) $\frac{10}{30}$ = ________

D) Simplify the fractions.

1) $\frac{10}{20}$ = ____________ 2) $\frac{5}{15}$ = ____________ 3) $\frac{12}{24}$ = ____________ 4) $\frac{2}{12}$ = ____________

5) $\frac{6}{8}$ = ____________ 6) $\frac{8}{12}$ = ____________ 7) $\frac{10}{25}$ = ____________ 8) $\frac{15}{40}$ = ____________

9) $\frac{27}{36}$ = ____________ 10) $\frac{8}{10}$ = ____________ 11) $\frac{8}{64}$ = ____________ 12) $\frac{7}{42}$ = ____________

13) $\frac{9}{12}$ = ____________ 14) $\frac{28}{35}$ = ____________ 15) $\frac{6}{18}$ = ____________ 16) $\frac{36}{72}$ = ____________

17) $\frac{8}{24}$ = ____________ 18) $\frac{8}{40}$ = ____________ 19) $\frac{42}{56}$ = ____________ 20) $\frac{15}{18}$ = ____________

21) $\frac{18}{36}$ = ____________ 22) $\frac{9}{27}$ = ____________ 23) $\frac{6}{12}$ = ____________ 24) $\frac{18}{72}$ = ____________

25) $\frac{24}{48}$ = ____________ 26) $\frac{20}{25}$ = ____________ 27) $\frac{30}{36}$ = ____________ 28) $\frac{4}{12}$ = ____________

29) $\frac{8}{16}$ = ____________ 30) $\frac{16}{40}$ = ____________ 31) $\frac{4}{16}$ = ____________ 32) $\frac{35}{56}$ = ____________

E) Simplify the fractions.

1) $\frac{2}{12}$ = ____________ 2) $\frac{20}{32}$ = ____________ 3) $\frac{9}{15}$ = ____________ 4) $\frac{18}{27}$ = ____________

5) $\frac{6}{48}$ = ____________ 6) $\frac{3}{15}$ = ____________ 7) $\frac{10}{15}$ = ____________ 8) $\frac{36}{54}$ = ____________

9) $\frac{4}{8}$ = ____________ 10) $\frac{3}{9}$ = ____________ 11) $\frac{4}{10}$ = ____________ 12) $\frac{24}{64}$ = ____________

13) $\frac{6}{12}$ = ____________ 14) $\frac{6}{36}$ = ____________ 15) $\frac{16}{24}$ = ____________ 16) $\frac{21}{35}$ = ____________

17) $\frac{27}{72}$ = ____________ 18) $\frac{18}{24}$ = ____________ 19) $\frac{24}{36}$ = ____________ 20) $\frac{4}{6}$ = ____________

21) $\frac{15}{20}$ = ____________ 22) $\frac{32}{48}$ = ____________ 23) $\frac{14}{56}$ = ____________ 24) $\frac{10}{25}$ = ____________

25) $\frac{45}{54}$ = ____________ 26) $\frac{14}{21}$ = ____________ 27) $\frac{15}{25}$ = ____________ 28) $\frac{18}{72}$ = ____________

29) $\frac{24}{32}$ = ____________ 30) $\frac{25}{30}$ = ____________ 31) $\frac{5}{15}$ = ____________ 32) $\frac{4}{16}$ = ____________

F) Simplify the fractions.

1) $\frac{12}{18}$ = ________ 2) $\frac{15}{20}$ = ________ 3) $\frac{24}{40}$ = ________ 4) $\frac{16}{64}$ = ________

5) $\frac{24}{32}$ = ________ 6) $\frac{3}{9}$ = ________ 7) $\frac{10}{12}$ = ________ 8) $\frac{21}{42}$ = ________

9) $\frac{28}{56}$ = ________ 10) $\frac{10}{20}$ = ________ 11) $\frac{8}{24}$ = ________ 12) $\frac{2}{10}$ = ________

13) $\frac{21}{35}$ = ________ 14) $\frac{5}{40}$ = ________ 15) $\frac{8}{12}$ = ________ 16) $\frac{7}{28}$ = ________

17) $\frac{16}{24}$ = ________ 18) $\frac{27}{36}$ = ________ 19) $\frac{4}{16}$ = ________ 20) $\frac{16}{48}$ = ________

21) $\frac{7}{21}$ = ________ 22) $\frac{3}{15}$ = ________ 23) $\frac{10}{15}$ = ________ 24) $\frac{63}{72}$ = ________

25) $\frac{12}{16}$ = ________ 26) $\frac{3}{18}$ = ________ 27) $\frac{12}{20}$ = ________ 28) $\frac{9}{27}$ = ________

29) $\frac{16}{32}$ = ________ 30) $\frac{27}{45}$ = ________ 31) $\frac{7}{42}$ = ________ 32) $\frac{20}{40}$ = ________

G) Simplify the fractions.

1) $\frac{2}{6}$ = ____________
2) $\frac{10}{20}$ = ____________
3) $\frac{14}{35}$ = ____________
4) $\frac{6}{18}$ = ____________

5) $\frac{6}{30}$ = ____________
6) $\frac{16}{32}$ = ____________
7) $\frac{8}{24}$ = ____________
8) $\frac{8}{64}$ = ____________

9) $\frac{10}{15}$ = ____________
10) $\frac{4}{12}$ = ____________
11) $\frac{18}{24}$ = ____________
12) $\frac{6}{9}$ = ____________

13) $\frac{12}{30}$ = ____________
14) $\frac{54}{72}$ = ____________
15) $\frac{3}{12}$ = ____________
16) $\frac{8}{12}$ = ____________

17) $\frac{5}{20}$ = ____________
18) $\frac{7}{42}$ = ____________
19) $\frac{5}{25}$ = ____________
20) $\frac{12}{18}$ = ____________

21) $\frac{6}{48}$ = ____________
22) $\frac{15}{20}$ = ____________
23) $\frac{16}{20}$ = ____________
24) $\frac{8}{48}$ = ____________

25) $\frac{14}{21}$ = ____________
26) $\frac{15}{40}$ = ____________
27) $\frac{9}{12}$ = ____________
28) $\frac{7}{35}$ = ____________

29) $\frac{9}{18}$ = ____________
30) $\frac{5}{15}$ = ____________
31) $\frac{4}{32}$ = ____________
32) $\frac{2}{8}$ = ____________

H) Simplify the fractions.

1) $\frac{15}{40}$ = ________ 2) $\frac{2}{12}$ = ________ 3) $\frac{9}{36}$ = ________ 4) $\frac{18}{27}$ = ________

5) $\frac{32}{48}$ = ________ 6) $\frac{21}{28}$ = ________ 7) $\frac{10}{15}$ = ________ 8) $\frac{28}{32}$ = ________

9) $\frac{4}{20}$ = ________ 10) $\frac{20}{30}$ = ________ 11) $\frac{7}{35}$ = ________ 12) $\frac{8}{32}$ = ________

13) $\frac{14}{21}$ = ________ 14) $\frac{35}{40}$ = ________ 15) $\frac{40}{48}$ = ________ 16) $\frac{14}{16}$ = ________

17) $\frac{4}{16}$ = ________ 18) $\frac{8}{24}$ = ________ 19) $\frac{2}{10}$ = ________ 20) $\frac{15}{20}$ = ________

21) $\frac{9}{72}$ = ________ 22) $\frac{5}{15}$ = ________ 23) $\frac{12}{30}$ = ________ 24) $\frac{14}{42}$ = ________

25) $\frac{15}{30}$ = ________ 26) $\frac{12}{24}$ = ________ 27) $\frac{42}{48}$ = ________ 28) $\frac{6}{15}$ = ________

29) $\frac{56}{64}$ = ________ 30) $\frac{16}{24}$ = ________ 31) $\frac{15}{25}$ = ________ 32) $\frac{2}{6}$ = ________

I) Simplify the fractions.

1) $\frac{7}{21}$ = ________ 2) $\frac{5}{25}$ = ________ 3) $\frac{28}{32}$ = ________ 4) $\frac{8}{48}$ = ________

5) $\frac{18}{30}$ = ________ 6) $\frac{6}{8}$ = ________ 7) $\frac{45}{72}$ = ________ 8) $\frac{3}{9}$ = ________

9) $\frac{7}{42}$ = ________ 10) $\frac{10}{15}$ = ________ 11) $\frac{21}{35}$ = ________ 12) $\frac{8}{24}$ = ________

13) $\frac{14}{16}$ = ________ 14) $\frac{6}{9}$ = ________ 15) $\frac{8}{20}$ = ________ 16) $\frac{15}{20}$ = ________

17) $\frac{24}{32}$ = ________ 18) $\frac{10}{20}$ = ________ 19) $\frac{20}{32}$ = ________ 20) $\frac{4}{12}$ = ________

21) $\frac{18}{27}$ = ________ 22) $\frac{8}{32}$ = ________ 23) $\frac{24}{30}$ = ________ 24) $\frac{35}{56}$ = ________

25) $\frac{10}{12}$ = ________ 26) $\frac{6}{16}$ = ________ 27) $\frac{20}{25}$ = ________ 28) $\frac{4}{16}$ = ________

29) $\frac{6}{18}$ = ________ 30) $\frac{8}{12}$ = ________ 31) $\frac{27}{54}$ = ________ 32) $\frac{2}{8}$ = ________

J) Simplify the fractions.

1) $\frac{1}{4}$ = ______ 2) $\frac{4}{12}$ = ______ 3) $\frac{10}{12}$ = ______ 4) $\frac{14}{21}$ = ______

5) $\frac{12}{20}$ = ______ 6) $\frac{12}{16}$ = ______ 7) $\frac{18}{24}$ = ______ 8) $\frac{18}{48}$ = ______

9) $\frac{16}{40}$ = ______ 10) $\frac{12}{24}$ = ______ 11) $\frac{6}{30}$ = ______ 12) $\frac{4}{16}$ = ______

13) $\frac{10}{15}$ = ______ 14) $\frac{7}{42}$ = ______ 15) $\frac{12}{30}$ = ______ 16) $\frac{5}{20}$ = ______

17) $\frac{6}{18}$ = ______ 18) $\frac{6}{12}$ = ______ 19) $\frac{2}{6}$ = ______ 20) $\frac{8}{64}$ = ______

21) $\frac{32}{40}$ = ______ 22) $\frac{10}{20}$ = ______ 23) $\frac{15}{20}$ = ______ 24) $\frac{10}{25}$ = ______

25) $\frac{27}{54}$ = ______ 26) $\frac{4}{32}$ = ______ 27) $\frac{7}{21}$ = ______ 28) $\frac{8}{12}$ = ______

29) $\frac{8}{16}$ = ______ 30) $\frac{24}{30}$ = ______ 31) $\frac{36}{72}$ = ______ 32) $\frac{6}{36}$ = ______

K) Simplify the fractions.

1) $\frac{162}{24}$ = ______

2) $\frac{75}{24}$ = ______

3) $\frac{6}{12}$ = ______

4) $\frac{300}{40}$ = ______

5) $\frac{82}{12}$ = ______

6) $\frac{6}{10}$ = ______

7) $\frac{174}{18}$ = ______

8) $\frac{186}{48}$ = ______

9) $\frac{66}{18}$ = ______

10) $\frac{224}{35}$ = ______

11) $\frac{140}{21}$ = ______

12) $\frac{165}{20}$ = ______

13) $\frac{140}{15}$ = ______

14) $\frac{12}{24}$ = ______

15) $\frac{30}{48}$ = ______

16) $\frac{280}{30}$ = ______

17) $\frac{85}{25}$ = ______

18) $\frac{304}{40}$ = ______

19) $\frac{26}{8}$ = ______

20) $\frac{333}{54}$ = ______

21) $\frac{8}{12}$ = ______

22) $\frac{376}{64}$ = ______

23) $\frac{20}{24}$ = ______

24) $\frac{48}{64}$ = ______

25) $\frac{84}{18}$ = ______

26) $\frac{3}{12}$ = ______

27) $\frac{138}{15}$ = ______

28) $\frac{90}{20}$ = ______

29) $\frac{352}{40}$ = ______

30) $\frac{51}{9}$ = ______

31) $\frac{32}{64}$ = ______

32) $\frac{16}{40}$ = ______

L) Simplify the fractions.

1) $\frac{216}{32}$ = ________ 2) $\frac{204}{30}$ = ________ 3) $\frac{21}{24}$ = ________ 4) $\frac{116}{12}$ = ________

5) $\frac{32}{40}$ = ________ 6) $\frac{8}{24}$ = ________ 7) $\frac{42}{9}$ = ________ 8) $\frac{15}{40}$ = ________

9) $\frac{75}{12}$ = ________ 10) $\frac{544}{64}$ = ________ 11) $\frac{82}{12}$ = ________ 12) $\frac{128}{24}$ = ________

13) $\frac{204}{24}$ = ________ 14) $\frac{7}{35}$ = ________ 15) $\frac{145}{15}$ = ________ 16) $\frac{168}{20}$ = ________

17) $\frac{20}{8}$ = ________ 18) $\frac{224}{64}$ = ________ 19) $\frac{450}{54}$ = ________ 20) $\frac{8}{10}$ = ________

21) $\frac{7}{42}$ = ________ 22) $\frac{3}{9}$ = ________ 23) $\frac{520}{64}$ = ________ 24) $\frac{21}{28}$ = ________

25) $\frac{81}{15}$ = ________ 26) $\frac{4}{12}$ = ________ 27) $\frac{108}{32}$ = ________ 28) $\frac{16}{48}$ = ________

29) $\frac{306}{36}$ = ________ 30) $\frac{9}{27}$ = ________ 31) $\frac{21}{42}$ = ________ 32) $\frac{4}{16}$ = ________

M) Simplify the fractions.

1) $\frac{55}{15}$ = ______	2) $\frac{231}{35}$ = ______	3) $\frac{32}{64}$ = ______	4) $\frac{18}{30}$ = ______
5) $\frac{52}{12}$ = ______	6) $\frac{3}{12}$ = ______	7) $\frac{9}{18}$ = ______	8) $\frac{16}{24}$ = ______
9) $\frac{128}{40}$ = ______	10) $\frac{273}{42}$ = ______	11) $\frac{455}{56}$ = ______	12) $\frac{5}{20}$ = ______
13) $\frac{6}{18}$ = ______	14) $\frac{16}{40}$ = ______	15) $\frac{2}{6}$ = ______	16) $\frac{16}{32}$ = ______
17) $\frac{6}{24}$ = ______	18) $\frac{10}{15}$ = ______	19) $\frac{114}{16}$ = ______	20) $\frac{91}{28}$ = ______
21) $\frac{119}{35}$ = ______	22) $\frac{315}{42}$ = ______	23) $\frac{35}{42}$ = ______	24) $\frac{12}{18}$ = ______
25) $\frac{511}{56}$ = ______	26) $\frac{114}{24}$ = ______	27) $\frac{22}{10}$ = ______	28) $\frac{4}{6}$ = ______
29) $\frac{2}{10}$ = ______	30) $\frac{138}{36}$ = ______	31) $\frac{8}{32}$ = ______	32) $\frac{222}{24}$ = ______

N) Simplify the fractions.

1) $\frac{21}{42}$ = ______ 2) $\frac{333}{45}$ = ______ 3) $\frac{21}{28}$ = ______ 4) $\frac{560}{64}$ = ______

5) $\frac{8}{24}$ = ______ 6) $\frac{2}{12}$ = ______ 7) $\frac{28}{8}$ = ______ 8) $\frac{12}{30}$ = ______

9) $\frac{172}{32}$ = ______ 10) $\frac{46}{6}$ = ______ 11) $\frac{8}{16}$ = ______ 12) $\frac{7}{35}$ = ______

13) $\frac{24}{36}$ = ______ 14) $\frac{91}{21}$ = ______ 15) $\frac{12}{16}$ = ______ 16) $\frac{312}{40}$ = ______

17) $\frac{207}{36}$ = ______ 18) $\frac{147}{18}$ = ______ 19) $\frac{7}{21}$ = ______ 20) $\frac{408}{48}$ = ______

21) $\frac{145}{15}$ = ______ 22) $\frac{6}{12}$ = ______ 23) $\frac{75}{18}$ = ______ 24) $\frac{150}{24}$ = ______

25) $\frac{36}{10}$ = ______ 26) $\frac{9}{27}$ = ______ 27) $\frac{140}{42}$ = ______ 28) $\frac{84}{15}$ = ______

29) $\frac{161}{28}$ = ______ 30) $\frac{28}{32}$ = ______ 31) $\frac{8}{20}$ = ______ 32) $\frac{252}{27}$ = ______

O) Simplify the fractions.

1) $\frac{2}{4}$ = ______ 2) $\frac{4}{24}$ = ______ 3) $\frac{8}{32}$ = ______ 4) $\frac{21}{35}$ = ______

5) $\frac{230}{40}$ = ______ 6) $\frac{168}{48}$ = ______ 7) $\frac{21}{9}$ = ______ 8) $\frac{84}{24}$ = ______

9) $\frac{21}{24}$ = ______ 10) $\frac{196}{21}$ = ______ 11) $\frac{30}{12}$ = ______ 12) $\frac{6}{12}$ = ______

13) $\frac{8}{64}$ = ______ 14) $\frac{182}{21}$ = ______ 15) $\frac{4}{20}$ = ______ 16) $\frac{69}{12}$ = ______

17) $\frac{264}{32}$ = ______ 18) $\frac{6}{36}$ = ______ 19) $\frac{64}{10}$ = ______ 20) $\frac{16}{32}$ = ______

21) $\frac{9}{27}$ = ______ 22) $\frac{165}{20}$ = ______ 23) $\frac{132}{24}$ = ______ 24) $\frac{65}{25}$ = ______

25) $\frac{2}{6}$ = ______ 26) $\frac{15}{40}$ = ______ 27) $\frac{15}{20}$ = ______ 28) $\frac{20}{40}$ = ______

29) $\frac{58}{10}$ = ______ 30) $\frac{140}{15}$ = ______ 31) $\frac{45}{54}$ = ______ 32) $\frac{12}{16}$ = ______

P) Simplify the fractions.

1) $\frac{10}{15}$ = ____________

2) $\frac{2}{12}$ = ____________

3) $\frac{285}{40}$ = ____________

4) $\frac{10}{20}$ = ____________

5) $\frac{64}{10}$ = ____________

6) $\frac{189}{28}$ = ____________

7) $\frac{87}{9}$ = ____________

8) $\frac{220}{30}$ = ____________

9) $\frac{35}{56}$ = ____________

10) $\frac{49}{56}$ = ____________

11) $\frac{114}{30}$ = ____________

12) $\frac{144}{27}$ = ____________

13) $\frac{44}{12}$ = ____________

14) $\frac{126}{28}$ = ____________

15) $\frac{69}{12}$ = ____________

16) $\frac{28}{56}$ = ____________

17) $\frac{14}{21}$ = ____________

18) $\frac{108}{45}$ = ____________

19) $\frac{35}{42}$ = ____________

20) $\frac{154}{28}$ = ____________

21) $\frac{4}{12}$ = ____________

22) $\frac{82}{10}$ = ____________

23) $\frac{165}{40}$ = ____________

24) $\frac{138}{36}$ = ____________

25) $\frac{27}{72}$ = ____________

26) $\frac{165}{30}$ = ____________

27) $\frac{171}{27}$ = ____________

28) $\frac{329}{35}$ = ____________

29) $\frac{54}{8}$ = ____________

30) $\frac{132}{18}$ = ____________

31) $\frac{21}{28}$ = ____________

32) $\frac{24}{48}$ = ____________

Q) Simplify the fractions.

1) $\frac{6}{18}$ = ________

2) $\frac{12}{16}$ = ________

3) $\frac{16}{40}$ = ________

4) $\frac{110}{20}$ = ________

5) $\frac{10}{16}$ = ________

6) $\frac{105}{30}$ = ________

7) $\frac{12}{18}$ = ________

8) $\frac{276}{32}$ = ________

9) $\frac{198}{36}$ = ________

10) $\frac{36}{45}$ = ________

11) $\frac{51}{9}$ = ________

12) $\frac{30}{36}$ = ________

13) $\frac{147}{28}$ = ________

14) $\frac{48}{18}$ = ________

15) $\frac{4}{20}$ = ________

16) $\frac{171}{18}$ = ________

17) $\frac{212}{32}$ = ________

18) $\frac{7}{21}$ = ________

19) $\frac{8}{20}$ = ________

20) $\frac{6}{36}$ = ________

21) $\frac{93}{12}$ = ________

22) $\frac{416}{64}$ = ________

23) $\frac{497}{56}$ = ________

24) $\frac{69}{15}$ = ________

25) $\frac{126}{36}$ = ________

26) $\frac{128}{48}$ = ________

27) $\frac{20}{32}$ = ________

28) $\frac{99}{12}$ = ________

29) $\frac{28}{35}$ = ________

30) $\frac{8}{24}$ = ________

31) $\frac{16}{20}$ = ________

32) $\frac{18}{54}$ = ________

R) Simplify the fractions.

1) $\frac{28}{12}$ = ________ 2) $\frac{6}{8}$ = ________ 3) $\frac{423}{72}$ = ________ 4) $\frac{16}{20}$ = ________

5) $\frac{12}{16}$ = ________ 6) $\frac{420}{56}$ = ________ 7) $\frac{450}{54}$ = ________ 8) $\frac{12}{18}$ = ________

9) $\frac{224}{42}$ = ________ 10) $\frac{64}{24}$ = ________ 11) $\frac{184}{32}$ = ________ 12) $\frac{350}{56}$ = ________

13) $\frac{133}{35}$ = ________ 14) $\frac{336}{40}$ = ________ 15) $\frac{20}{40}$ = ________ 16) $\frac{16}{32}$ = ________

17) $\frac{165}{30}$ = ________ 18) $\frac{171}{27}$ = ________ 19) $\frac{10}{30}$ = ________ 20) $\frac{126}{36}$ = ________

21) $\frac{18}{45}$ = ________ 22) $\frac{9}{27}$ = ________ 23) $\frac{4}{12}$ = ________ 24) $\frac{522}{72}$ = ________

25) $\frac{8}{16}$ = ________ 26) $\frac{24}{48}$ = ________ 27) $\frac{12}{20}$ = ________ 28) $\frac{39}{9}$ = ________

29) $\frac{132}{24}$ = ________ 30) $\frac{2}{8}$ = ________ 31) $\frac{21}{42}$ = ________ 32) $\frac{62}{10}$ = ________

S) Simplify the fractions.

1) $\frac{23}{3}$ = ________

2) $\frac{8}{12}$ = ________

3) $\frac{9}{12}$ = ________

4) $\frac{15}{25}$ = ________

5) $\frac{12}{24}$ = ________

6) $\frac{30}{40}$ = ________

7) $\frac{2}{8}$ = ________

8) $\frac{222}{36}$ = ________

9) $\frac{138}{30}$ = ________

10) $\frac{99}{27}$ = ________

11) $\frac{7}{21}$ = ________

12) $\frac{198}{54}$ = ________

13) $\frac{16}{20}$ = ________

14) $\frac{68}{16}$ = ________

15) $\frac{24}{32}$ = ________

16) $\frac{318}{48}$ = ________

17) $\frac{5}{15}$ = ________

18) $\frac{36}{45}$ = ________

19) $\frac{9}{18}$ = ________

20) $\frac{424}{48}$ = ________

21) $\frac{144}{40}$ = ________

22) $\frac{72}{27}$ = ________

23) $\frac{20}{40}$ = ________

24) $\frac{18}{36}$ = ________

25) $\frac{105}{20}$ = ________

26) $\frac{9}{27}$ = ________

27) $\frac{16}{48}$ = ________

28) $\frac{12}{15}$ = ________

29) $\frac{162}{72}$ = ________

30) $\frac{24}{40}$ = ________

31) $\frac{8}{16}$ = ________

32) $\frac{132}{18}$ = ________

T) Simplify the fractions.

1) $\frac{292}{32}$ = ________

2) $\frac{230}{25}$ = ________

3) $\frac{21}{24}$ = ________

4) $\frac{392}{48}$ = ________

5) $\frac{18}{27}$ = ________

6) $\frac{9}{12}$ = ________

7) $\frac{132}{24}$ = ________

8) $\frac{295}{40}$ = ________

9) $\frac{66}{30}$ = ________

10) $\frac{69}{9}$ = ________

11) $\frac{100}{16}$ = ________

12) $\frac{348}{36}$ = ________

13) $\frac{12}{16}$ = ________

14) $\frac{6}{18}$ = ________

15) $\frac{2}{8}$ = ________

16) $\frac{343}{35}$ = ________

17) $\frac{630}{72}$ = ________

18) $\frac{423}{45}$ = ________

19) $\frac{105}{42}$ = ________

20) $\frac{66}{9}$ = ________

21) $\frac{68}{8}$ = ________

22) $\frac{60}{16}$ = ________

23) $\frac{14}{56}$ = ________

24) $\frac{12}{18}$ = ________

25) $\frac{3}{18}$ = ________

26) $\frac{138}{15}$ = ________

27) $\frac{30}{8}$ = ________

28) $\frac{20}{40}$ = ________

29) $\frac{77}{21}$ = ________

30) $\frac{63}{18}$ = ________

31) $\frac{294}{35}$ = ________

32) $\frac{25}{40}$ = ________

U) Simplify the fractions.

1) $\frac{168}{18}$ = ______ 2) $\frac{68}{16}$ = ______ 3) $\frac{322}{56}$ = ______ 4) $\frac{24}{48}$ = ______

5) $\frac{54}{9}$ = ______ 6) $\frac{120}{20}$ = ______ 7) $\frac{56}{8}$ = ______ 8) $\frac{54}{6}$ = ______

9) $\frac{504}{56}$ = ______ 10) $\frac{140}{20}$ = ______ 11) $\frac{72}{12}$ = ______ 12) $\frac{120}{30}$ = ______

13) $\frac{270}{45}$ = ______ 14) $\frac{18}{54}$ = ______ 15) $\frac{5}{15}$ = ______ 16) $\frac{22}{8}$ = ______

17) $\frac{144}{72}$ = ______ 18) $\frac{112}{35}$ = ______ 19) $\frac{36}{48}$ = ______ 20) $\frac{44}{12}$ = ______

21) $\frac{168}{28}$ = ______ 22) $\frac{168}{42}$ = ______ 23) $\frac{135}{27}$ = ______ 24) $\frac{352}{48}$ = ______

25) $\frac{64}{16}$ = ______ 26) $\frac{6}{48}$ = ______ 27) $\frac{186}{30}$ = ______ 28) $\frac{162}{72}$ = ______

29) $\frac{6}{10}$ = ______ 30) $\frac{48}{24}$ = ______ 31) $\frac{32}{16}$ = ______ 32) $\frac{24}{12}$ = ______

V) Simplify the fractions.

1) $\frac{120}{24}$ = ________ 2) $\frac{120}{40}$ = ________ 3) $\frac{18}{45}$ = ________ 4) $\frac{72}{18}$ = ________

5) $\frac{2}{6}$ = ________ 6) $\frac{216}{24}$ = ________ 7) $\frac{144}{48}$ = ________ 8) $\frac{8}{12}$ = ________

9) $\frac{6}{8}$ = ________ 10) $\frac{60}{15}$ = ________ 11) $\frac{10}{30}$ = ________ 12) $\frac{160}{40}$ = ________

13) $\frac{45}{72}$ = ________ 14) $\frac{18}{27}$ = ________ 15) $\frac{48}{24}$ = ________ 16) $\frac{24}{64}$ = ________

17) $\frac{238}{35}$ = ________ 18) $\frac{108}{27}$ = ________ 19) $\frac{2}{8}$ = ________ 20) $\frac{6}{18}$ = ________

21) $\frac{375}{40}$ = ________ 22) $\frac{175}{35}$ = ________ 23) $\frac{108}{12}$ = ________ 24) $\frac{280}{40}$ = ________

25) $\frac{12}{24}$ = ________ 26) $\frac{8}{16}$ = ________ 27) $\frac{27}{9}$ = ________ 28) $\frac{185}{30}$ = ________

29) $\frac{125}{25}$ = ________ 30) $\frac{10}{12}$ = ________ 31) $\frac{15}{20}$ = ________ 32) $\frac{24}{32}$ = ________

W) Simplify the fractions.

1) $\frac{12}{18}$ = ____________ 2) $\frac{264}{32}$ = ____________ 3) $\frac{48}{24}$ = ____________ 4) $\frac{4}{12}$ = ____________

5) $\frac{240}{30}$ = ____________ 6) $\frac{6}{10}$ = ____________ 7) $\frac{36}{48}$ = ____________ 8) $\frac{42}{12}$ = ____________

9) $\frac{72}{24}$ = ____________ 10) $\frac{120}{15}$ = ____________ 11) $\frac{216}{72}$ = ____________ 12) $\frac{18}{27}$ = ____________

13) $\frac{75}{12}$ = ____________ 14) $\frac{423}{45}$ = ____________ 15) $\frac{232}{48}$ = ____________ 16) $\frac{8}{24}$ = ____________

17) $\frac{20}{10}$ = ____________ 18) $\frac{10}{40}$ = ____________ 19) $\frac{45}{54}$ = ____________ 20) $\frac{102}{12}$ = ____________

21) $\frac{7}{28}$ = ____________ 22) $\frac{12}{6}$ = ____________ 23) $\frac{75}{30}$ = ____________ 24) $\frac{192}{20}$ = ____________

25) $\frac{8}{32}$ = ____________ 26) $\frac{88}{24}$ = ____________ 27) $\frac{130}{16}$ = ____________ 28) $\frac{301}{35}$ = ____________

29) $\frac{9}{36}$ = ____________ 30) $\frac{72}{9}$ = ____________ 31) $\frac{36}{16}$ = ____________ 32) $\frac{336}{48}$ = ____________

X) Simplify the fractions.

1) $\frac{198}{36}$ = ________ 2) $\frac{49}{56}$ = ________ 3) $\frac{56}{8}$ = ________ 4) $\frac{240}{40}$ = ________

5) $\frac{12}{18}$ = ________ 6) $\frac{72}{36}$ = ________ 7) $\frac{65}{25}$ = ________ 8) $\frac{40}{6}$ = ________

9) $\frac{245}{35}$ = ________ 10) $\frac{144}{72}$ = ________ 11) $\frac{100}{16}$ = ________ 12) $\frac{324}{54}$ = ________

13) $\frac{30}{9}$ = ________ 14) $\frac{60}{20}$ = ________ 15) $\frac{48}{64}$ = ________ 16) $\frac{396}{54}$ = ________

17) $\frac{10}{25}$ = ________ 18) $\frac{7}{21}$ = ________ 19) $\frac{74}{10}$ = ________ 20) $\frac{441}{72}$ = ________

21) $\frac{252}{36}$ = ________ 22) $\frac{14}{6}$ = ________ 23) $\frac{7}{42}$ = ________ 24) $\frac{108}{27}$ = ________

25) $\frac{144}{30}$ = ________ 26) $\frac{272}{48}$ = ________ 27) $\frac{9}{36}$ = ________ 28) $\frac{18}{24}$ = ________

29) $\frac{96}{48}$ = ________ 30) $\frac{192}{24}$ = ________ 31) $\frac{102}{30}$ = ________ 32) $\frac{108}{12}$ = ________

Y) Simplify the fractions.

1) $\frac{100}{25}$ = ________ 2) $\frac{48}{12}$ = ________ 3) $\frac{12}{16}$ = ________ 4) $\frac{392}{56}$ = ________

5) $\frac{133}{21}$ = ________ 6) $\frac{40}{10}$ = ________ 7) $\frac{28}{32}$ = ________ 8) $\frac{90}{27}$ = ________

9) $\frac{210}{35}$ = ________ 10) $\frac{20}{24}$ = ________ 11) $\frac{48}{8}$ = ________ 12) $\frac{96}{24}$ = ________

13) $\frac{8}{12}$ = ________ 14) $\frac{96}{16}$ = ________ 15) $\frac{135}{27}$ = ________ 16) $\frac{40}{20}$ = ________

17) $\frac{438}{48}$ = ________ 18) $\frac{16}{24}$ = ________ 19) $\frac{248}{48}$ = ________ 20) $\frac{144}{24}$ = ________

21) $\frac{111}{12}$ = ________ 22) $\frac{3}{24}$ = ________ 23) $\frac{152}{24}$ = ________ 24) $\frac{9}{45}$ = ________

25) $\frac{156}{18}$ = ________ 26) $\frac{204}{24}$ = ________ 27) $\frac{174}{18}$ = ________ 28) $\frac{24}{30}$ = ________

29) $\frac{42}{56}$ = ________ 30) $\frac{27}{12}$ = ________ 31) $\frac{188}{20}$ = ________ 32) $\frac{252}{42}$ = ________

Z) Simplify the fractions.

1) $\frac{126}{27}$ = ________ 2) $\frac{100}{25}$ = ________ 3) $\frac{3}{9}$ = ________ 4) $\frac{8}{16}$ = ________

5) $\frac{216}{24}$ = ________ 6) $\frac{96}{12}$ = ________ 7) $\frac{36}{72}$ = ________ 8) $\frac{35}{42}$ = ________

9) $\frac{245}{28}$ = ________ 10) $\frac{4}{12}$ = ________ 11) $\frac{145}{25}$ = ________ 12) $\frac{81}{27}$ = ________

13) $\frac{216}{72}$ = ________ 14) $\frac{111}{12}$ = ________ 15) $\frac{78}{15}$ = ________ 16) $\frac{24}{48}$ = ________

17) $\frac{216}{27}$ = ________ 18) $\frac{14}{16}$ = ________ 19) $\frac{182}{28}$ = ________ 20) $\frac{108}{12}$ = ________

21) $\frac{2}{10}$ = ________ 22) $\frac{3}{18}$ = ________ 23) $\frac{6}{24}$ = ________ 24) $\frac{40}{64}$ = ________

25) $\frac{261}{45}$ = ________ 26) $\frac{24}{6}$ = ________ 27) $\frac{156}{16}$ = ________ 28) $\frac{84}{12}$ = ________

29) $\frac{36}{18}$ = ________ 30) $\frac{128}{32}$ = ________ 31) $\frac{14}{35}$ = ________ 32) $\frac{40}{48}$ = ________

AA) Simplify the fractions.

1) $\frac{192}{32}$ = ________ 2) $\frac{88}{12}$ = ________ 3) $\frac{22}{10}$ = ________ 4) $\frac{175}{42}$ = ________

5) $\frac{135}{27}$ = ________ 6) $\frac{144}{24}$ = ________ 7) $\frac{210}{35}$ = ________ 8) $\frac{168}{24}$ = ________

9) $\frac{532}{56}$ = ________ 10) $\frac{224}{32}$ = ________ 11) $\frac{104}{16}$ = ________ 12) $\frac{8}{12}$ = ________

13) $\frac{384}{48}$ = ________ 14) $\frac{320}{40}$ = ________ 15) $\frac{72}{12}$ = ________ 16) $\frac{6}{30}$ = ________

17) $\frac{46}{6}$ = ________ 18) $\frac{10}{20}$ = ________ 19) $\frac{256}{32}$ = ________ 20) $\frac{48}{16}$ = ________

21) $\frac{245}{35}$ = ________ 22) $\frac{130}{15}$ = ________ 23) $\frac{352}{64}$ = ________ 24) $\frac{80}{12}$ = ________

25) $\frac{512}{64}$ = ________ 26) $\frac{12}{30}$ = ________ 27) $\frac{55}{15}$ = ________ 28) $\frac{20}{30}$ = ________

29) $\frac{6}{8}$ = ________ 30) $\frac{639}{72}$ = ________ 31) $\frac{8}{24}$ = ________ 32) $\frac{360}{40}$ = ________

BB) Simplify the fractions.

1) $\frac{90}{30}$ = ______ 2) $\frac{36}{72}$ = ______ 3) $\frac{212}{24}$ = ______ 4) $\frac{152}{20}$ = ______

5) $\frac{279}{36}$ = ______ 6) $\frac{360}{40}$ = ______ 7) $\frac{4}{6}$ = ______ 8) $\frac{108}{36}$ = ______

9) $\frac{3}{9}$ = ______ 10) $\frac{250}{40}$ = ______ 11) $\frac{72}{8}$ = ______ 12) $\frac{45}{15}$ = ______

13) $\frac{360}{48}$ = ______ 14) $\frac{18}{27}$ = ______ 15) $\frac{177}{24}$ = ______ 16) $\frac{240}{40}$ = ______

17) $\frac{2}{8}$ = ______ 18) $\frac{432}{48}$ = ______ 19) $\frac{216}{24}$ = ______ 20) $\frac{42}{48}$ = ______

21) $\frac{162}{18}$ = ______ 22) $\frac{100}{20}$ = ______ 23) $\frac{280}{40}$ = ______ 24) $\frac{270}{54}$ = ______

25) $\frac{136}{16}$ = ______ 26) $\frac{72}{27}$ = ______ 27) $\frac{531}{72}$ = ______ 28) $\frac{148}{16}$ = ______

29) $\frac{144}{16}$ = ______ 30) $\frac{210}{36}$ = ______ 31) $\frac{52}{12}$ = ______ 32) $\frac{75}{25}$ = ______

CC) Simplify the fractions.

1) $\frac{24}{36}$ = ____ 2) $\frac{56}{28}$ = ____ 3) $\frac{46}{6}$ = ____ 4) $\frac{258}{48}$ = ____

5) $\frac{189}{35}$ = ____ 6) $\frac{210}{30}$ = ____ 7) $\frac{133}{35}$ = ____ 8) $\frac{6}{12}$ = ____

9) $\frac{8}{12}$ = ____ 10) $\frac{144}{64}$ = ____ 11) $\frac{72}{27}$ = ____ 12) $\frac{44}{12}$ = ____

13) $\frac{27}{72}$ = ____ 14) $\frac{84}{16}$ = ____ 15) $\frac{161}{35}$ = ____ 16) $\frac{440}{48}$ = ____

17) $\frac{213}{24}$ = ____ 18) $\frac{216}{27}$ = ____ 19) $\frac{6}{24}$ = ____ 20) $\frac{198}{27}$ = ____

21) $\frac{100}{20}$ = ____ 22) $\frac{14}{42}$ = ____ 23) $\frac{315}{72}$ = ____ 24) $\frac{63}{12}$ = ____

25) $\frac{45}{15}$ = ____ 26) $\frac{324}{36}$ = ____ 27) $\frac{10}{30}$ = ____ 28) $\frac{153}{27}$ = ____

29) $\frac{120}{24}$ = ____ 30) $\frac{3}{12}$ = ____ 31) $\frac{147}{15}$ = ____ 32) $\frac{60}{15}$ = ____

DD) Simplify the fractions.

1) $\frac{57}{8}$ = ________ 2) $\frac{160}{32}$ = ________ 3) $\frac{32}{40}$ = ________ 4) $\frac{92}{24}$ = ________

5) $\frac{12}{16}$ = ________ 6) $\frac{49}{56}$ = ________ 7) $\frac{48}{24}$ = ________ 8) $\frac{4}{8}$ = ________

9) $\frac{114}{18}$ = ________ 10) $\frac{9}{15}$ = ________ 11) $\frac{36}{48}$ = ________ 12) $\frac{132}{30}$ = ________

13) $\frac{36}{54}$ = ________ 14) $\frac{98}{16}$ = ________ 15) $\frac{33}{9}$ = ________ 16) $\frac{32}{8}$ = ________

17) $\frac{230}{30}$ = ________ 18) $\frac{80}{25}$ = ________ 19) $\frac{280}{40}$ = ________ 20) $\frac{15}{20}$ = ________

21) $\frac{156}{18}$ = ________ 22) $\frac{24}{64}$ = ________ 23) $\frac{32}{48}$ = ________ 24) $\frac{108}{12}$ = ________

25) $\frac{110}{20}$ = ________ 26) $\frac{245}{35}$ = ________ 27) $\frac{60}{20}$ = ________ 28) $\frac{140}{24}$ = ________

29) $\frac{3}{12}$ = ________ 30) $\frac{224}{32}$ = ________ 31) $\frac{98}{21}$ = ________ 32) $\frac{162}{27}$ = ________

EE) Simplify the fractions.

1) $\frac{360}{60}$ = ______ 2) $\frac{14}{42}$ = ______ 3) $\frac{504}{126}$ = ______ 4) $\frac{60}{8}$ = ______

5) $\frac{420}{60}$ = ______ 6) $\frac{94}{16}$ = ______ 7) $\frac{792}{128}$ = ______ 8) $\frac{7}{14}$ = ______

9) $\frac{6}{18}$ = ______ 10) $\frac{21}{27}$ = ______ 11) $\frac{204}{68}$ = ______ 12) $\frac{180}{56}$ = ______

13) $\frac{265}{50}$ = ______ 14) $\frac{186}{36}$ = ______ 15) $\frac{2}{36}$ = ______ 16) $\frac{120}{20}$ = ______

17) $\frac{108}{45}$ = ______ 18) $\frac{222}{42}$ = ______ 19) $\frac{480}{88}$ = ______ 20) $\frac{96}{48}$ = ______

21) $\frac{258}{26}$ = ______ 22) $\frac{270}{90}$ = ______ 23) $\frac{366}{57}$ = ______ 24) $\frac{300}{100}$ = ______

25) $\frac{282}{36}$ = ______ 26) $\frac{603}{171}$ = ______ 27) $\frac{24}{36}$ = ______ 28) $\frac{94}{24}$ = ______

29) $\frac{609}{63}$ = ______ 30) $\frac{9}{117}$ = ______ 31) $\frac{268}{28}$ = ______ 32) $\frac{56}{126}$ = ______

FF) Simplify the fractions.

1) $\frac{64}{24}$ = ______ 2) $\frac{492}{54}$ = ______ 3) $\frac{28}{84}$ = ______ 4) $\frac{655}{90}$ = ______

5) $\frac{36}{48}$ = ______ 6) $\frac{1665}{180}$ = ______ 7) $\frac{392}{56}$ = ______ 8) $\frac{450}{135}$ = ______

9) $\frac{150}{25}$ = ______ 10) $\frac{288}{32}$ = ______ 11) $\frac{16}{68}$ = ______ 12) $\frac{176}{22}$ = ______

13) $\frac{6}{12}$ = ______ 14) $\frac{513}{90}$ = ______ 15) $\frac{18}{36}$ = ______ 16) $\frac{27}{99}$ = ______

17) $\frac{198}{21}$ = ______ 18) $\frac{630}{105}$ = ______ 19) $\frac{57}{27}$ = ______ 20) $\frac{288}{48}$ = ______

21) $\frac{84}{133}$ = ______ 22) $\frac{360}{72}$ = ______ 23) $\frac{4}{6}$ = ______ 24) $\frac{610}{65}$ = ______

25) $\frac{406}{42}$ = ______ 26) $\frac{413}{98}$ = ______ 27) $\frac{275}{90}$ = ______ 28) $\frac{80}{40}$ = ______

29) $\frac{264}{40}$ = ______ 30) $\frac{148}{34}$ = ______ 31) $\frac{54}{72}$ = ______ 32) $\frac{360}{45}$ = ______

GG) Simplify the fractions.

1) $\frac{3}{9}$ = ___________ 2) $\frac{18}{84}$ = ___________ 3) $\frac{134}{40}$ = ___________ 4) $\frac{84}{15}$ = ___________

5) $\frac{800}{90}$ = ___________ 6) $\frac{243}{27}$ = ___________ 7) $\frac{32}{8}$ = ___________ 8) $\frac{400}{104}$ = ___________

9) $\frac{42}{119}$ = ___________ 10) $\frac{4}{16}$ = ___________ 11) $\frac{6}{24}$ = ___________ 12) $\frac{360}{63}$ = ___________

13) $\frac{198}{54}$ = ___________ 14) $\frac{88}{96}$ = ___________ 15) $\frac{150}{50}$ = ___________ 16) $\frac{36}{44}$ = ___________

17) $\frac{5}{80}$ = ___________ 18) $\frac{420}{60}$ = ___________ 19) $\frac{312}{48}$ = ___________ 20) $\frac{88}{32}$ = ___________

21) $\frac{189}{21}$ = ___________ 22) $\frac{675}{135}$ = ___________ 23) $\frac{1053}{117}$ = ___________ 24) $\frac{632}{128}$ = ___________

25) $\frac{3}{6}$ = ___________ 26) $\frac{474}{72}$ = ___________ 27) $\frac{612}{114}$ = ___________ 28) $\frac{340}{55}$ = ___________

29) $\frac{632}{72}$ = ___________ 30) $\frac{42}{108}$ = ___________ 31) $\frac{96}{120}$ = ___________ 32) $\frac{88}{34}$ = ___________

HH) Simplify the fractions.

1) $\frac{32}{16}$ = ______ 2) $\frac{9}{12}$ = ______ 3) $\frac{6}{12}$ = ______ 4) $\frac{945}{133}$ = ______

5) $\frac{90}{117}$ = ______ 6) $\frac{111}{27}$ = ______ 7) $\frac{220}{38}$ = ______ 8) $\frac{30}{32}$ = ______

9) $\frac{16}{44}$ = ______ 10) $\frac{259}{42}$ = ______ 11) $\frac{38}{4}$ = ______ 12) $\frac{270}{45}$ = ______

13) $\frac{600}{84}$ = ______ 14) $\frac{66}{30}$ = ______ 15) $\frac{105}{21}$ = ______ 16) $\frac{972}{108}$ = ______

17) $\frac{90}{108}$ = ______ 18) $\frac{520}{104}$ = ______ 19) $\frac{248}{80}$ = ______ 20) $\frac{14}{34}$ = ______

21) $\frac{45}{75}$ = ______ 22) $\frac{108}{27}$ = ______ 23) $\frac{360}{40}$ = ______ 24) $\frac{180}{24}$ = ______

25) $\frac{476}{119}$ = ______ 26) $\frac{351}{117}$ = ______ 27) $\frac{333}{72}$ = ______ 28) $\frac{24}{40}$ = ______

29) $\frac{352}{80}$ = ______ 30) $\frac{270}{90}$ = ______ 31) $\frac{18}{27}$ = ______ 32) $\frac{513}{171}$ = ______

II) Simplify the fractions.

1) $\frac{80}{88}$ = ________ 2) $\frac{18}{114}$ = ________ 3) $\frac{216}{24}$ = ________ 4) $\frac{360}{45}$ = ________

5) $\frac{25}{30}$ = ________ 6) $\frac{459}{144}$ = ________ 7) $\frac{6}{30}$ = ________ 8) $\frac{14}{63}$ = ________

9) $\frac{588}{84}$ = ________ 10) $\frac{7}{91}$ = ________ 11) $\frac{568}{104}$ = ________ 12) $\frac{16}{48}$ = ________

13) $\frac{312}{40}$ = ________ 14) $\frac{52}{72}$ = ________ 15) $\frac{222}{102}$ = ________ 16) $\frac{585}{60}$ = ________

17) $\frac{291}{42}$ = ________ 18) $\frac{3}{6}$ = ________ 19) $\frac{3}{60}$ = ________ 20) $\frac{567}{81}$ = ________

21) $\frac{336}{40}$ = ________ 22) $\frac{60}{20}$ = ________ 23) $\frac{45}{55}$ = ________ 24) $\frac{1064}{152}$ = ________

25) $\frac{45}{75}$ = ________ 26) $\frac{4}{16}$ = ________ 27) $\frac{196}{21}$ = ________ 28) $\frac{98}{49}$ = ________

29) $\frac{1112}{128}$ = ________ 30) $\frac{348}{102}$ = ________ 31) $\frac{240}{48}$ = ________ 32) $\frac{16}{28}$ = ________

JJ) Simplify the fractions.

1) $\frac{25}{10}$ = ______ 2) $\frac{225}{45}$ = ______ 3) $\frac{238}{119}$ = ______ 4) $\frac{80}{96}$ = ______

5) $\frac{48}{24}$ = ______ 6) $\frac{10}{30}$ = ______ 7) $\frac{78}{120}$ = ______ 8) $\frac{378}{49}$ = ______

9) $\frac{525}{75}$ = ______ 10) $\frac{312}{40}$ = ______ 11) $\frac{125}{15}$ = ______ 12) $\frac{540}{65}$ = ______

13) $\frac{152}{38}$ = ______ 14) $\frac{432}{72}$ = ______ 15) $\frac{108}{54}$ = ______ 16) $\frac{76}{32}$ = ______

17) $\frac{6}{12}$ = ______ 18) $\frac{27}{144}$ = ______ 19) $\frac{549}{72}$ = ______ 20) $\frac{336}{42}$ = ______

21) $\frac{42}{10}$ = ______ 22) $\frac{665}{77}$ = ______ 23) $\frac{285}{60}$ = ______ 24) $\frac{55}{95}$ = ______

25) $\frac{96}{48}$ = ______ 26) $\frac{294}{42}$ = ______ 27) $\frac{112}{119}$ = ______ 28) $\frac{630}{126}$ = ______

29) $\frac{7}{28}$ = ______ 30) $\frac{3}{9}$ = ______ 31) $\frac{20}{45}$ = ______ 32) $\frac{702}{117}$ = ______

KK) Simplify the fractions.

1) $\frac{60}{96}$ = __________

2) $\frac{272}{104}$ = __________

3) $\frac{180}{60}$ = __________

4) $\frac{95}{25}$ = __________

5) $\frac{990}{171}$ = __________

6) $\frac{840}{120}$ = __________

7) $\frac{360}{54}$ = __________

8) $\frac{6}{33}$ = __________

9) $\frac{42}{102}$ = __________

10) $\frac{168}{56}$ = __________

11) $\frac{196}{98}$ = __________

12) $\frac{480}{60}$ = __________

13) $\frac{9}{45}$ = __________

14) $\frac{84}{16}$ = __________

15) $\frac{624}{78}$ = __________

16) $\frac{378}{126}$ = __________

17) $\frac{12}{84}$ = __________

18) $\frac{702}{90}$ = __________

19) $\frac{90}{18}$ = __________

20) $\frac{54}{18}$ = __________

21) $\frac{336}{36}$ = __________

22) $\frac{144}{18}$ = __________

23) $\frac{576}{64}$ = __________

24) $\frac{497}{112}$ = __________

25) $\frac{624}{96}$ = __________

26) $\frac{39}{57}$ = __________

27) $\frac{750}{120}$ = __________

28) $\frac{528}{88}$ = __________

29) $\frac{690}{85}$ = __________

30) $\frac{732}{90}$ = __________

31) $\frac{882}{180}$ = __________

32) $\frac{171}{27}$ = __________

LL) Simplify the fractions.

1) $\frac{450}{90}$ = ________ 2) $\frac{560}{80}$ = ________ 3) $\frac{297}{99}$ = ________ 4) $\frac{5}{25}$ = ________

5) $\frac{1440}{160}$ = ________ 6) $\frac{1296}{144}$ = ________ 7) $\frac{408}{48}$ = ________ 8) $\frac{30}{34}$ = ________

9) $\frac{48}{24}$ = ________ 10) $\frac{510}{70}$ = ________ 11) $\frac{264}{48}$ = ________ 12) $\frac{6}{24}$ = ________

13) $\frac{144}{24}$ = ________ 14) $\frac{26}{38}$ = ________ 15) $\frac{477}{117}$ = ________ 16) $\frac{28}{36}$ = ________

17) $\frac{735}{105}$ = ________ 18) $\frac{576}{72}$ = ________ 19) $\frac{539}{77}$ = ________ 20) $\frac{48}{136}$ = ________

21) $\frac{78}{8}$ = ________ 22) $\frac{54}{18}$ = ________ 23) $\frac{10}{30}$ = ________ 24) $\frac{980}{140}$ = ________

25) $\frac{96}{48}$ = ________ 26) $\frac{76}{36}$ = ________ 27) $\frac{205}{35}$ = ________ 28) $\frac{210}{30}$ = ________

29) $\frac{567}{112}$ = ________ 30) $\frac{126}{14}$ = ________ 31) $\frac{8}{40}$ = ________ 32) $\frac{81}{108}$ = ________

MM) Simplify the fractions.

1) $\frac{56}{126}$ = ________ 2) $\frac{18}{72}$ = ________ 3) $\frac{416}{44}$ = ________ 4) $\frac{686}{98}$ = ________

5) $\frac{252}{42}$ = ________ 6) $\frac{90}{25}$ = ________ 7) $\frac{171}{51}$ = ________ 8) $\frac{36}{60}$ = ________

9) $\frac{88}{44}$ = ________ 10) $\frac{6}{24}$ = ________ 11) $\frac{8}{16}$ = ________ 12) $\frac{124}{32}$ = ________

13) $\frac{35}{98}$ = ________ 14) $\frac{800}{100}$ = ________ 15) $\frac{342}{108}$ = ________ 16) $\frac{28}{36}$ = ________

17) $\frac{285}{57}$ = ________ 18) $\frac{36}{72}$ = ________ 19) $\frac{60}{30}$ = ________ 20) $\frac{24}{60}$ = ________

21) $\frac{14}{16}$ = ________ 22) $\frac{226}{26}$ = ________ 23) $\frac{48}{9}$ = ________ 24) $\frac{84}{108}$ = ________

25) $\frac{1071}{153}$ = ________ 26) $\frac{64}{152}$ = ________ 27) $\frac{228}{60}$ = ________ 28) $\frac{22}{4}$ = ________

29) $\frac{328}{80}$ = ________ 30) $\frac{5}{15}$ = ________ 31) $\frac{522}{66}$ = ________ 32) $\frac{168}{24}$ = ________

NN) Simplify the fractions.

1) $\frac{220}{44}$ = ________

2) $\frac{720}{144}$ = ________

3) $\frac{6}{60}$ = ________

4) $\frac{1728}{180}$ = ________

5) $\frac{54}{84}$ = ________

6) $\frac{20}{24}$ = ________

7) $\frac{175}{35}$ = ________

8) $\frac{675}{75}$ = ________

9) $\frac{665}{95}$ = ________

10) $\frac{104}{12}$ = ________

11) $\frac{135}{15}$ = ________

12) $\frac{160}{48}$ = ________

13) $\frac{28}{36}$ = ________

14) $\frac{86}{34}$ = ________

15) $\frac{54}{63}$ = ________

16) $\frac{12}{60}$ = ________

17) $\frac{170}{65}$ = ________

18) $\frac{36}{108}$ = ________

19) $\frac{21}{45}$ = ________

20) $\frac{90}{15}$ = ________

21) $\frac{476}{77}$ = ________

22) $\frac{63}{72}$ = ________

23) $\frac{115}{20}$ = ________

24) $\frac{14}{24}$ = ________

25) $\frac{624}{84}$ = ________

26) $\frac{5}{10}$ = ________

27) $\frac{820}{95}$ = ________

28) $\frac{700}{140}$ = ________

29) $\frac{40}{64}$ = ________

30) $\frac{104}{52}$ = ________

31) $\frac{210}{30}$ = ________

32) $\frac{864}{144}$ = ________

OO) Simplify the fractions.

1) $\frac{927}{270}$ = ________ 2) $\frac{20}{110}$ = ________ 3) $\frac{138}{150}$ = ________ 4) $\frac{15}{75}$ = ________

5) $\frac{469}{84}$ = ________ 6) $\frac{95}{15}$ = ________ 7) $\frac{128}{28}$ = ________ 8) $\frac{63}{162}$ = ________

9) $\frac{4050}{450}$ = ________ 10) $\frac{4}{28}$ = ________ 11) $\frac{32}{4}$ = ________ 12) $\frac{1182}{120}$ = ________

13) $\frac{234}{39}$ = ________ 14) $\frac{1408}{400}$ = ________ 15) $\frac{230}{45}$ = ________ 16) $\frac{6}{32}$ = ________

17) $\frac{1728}{240}$ = ________ 18) $\frac{640}{80}$ = ________ 19) $\frac{360}{120}$ = ________ 20) $\frac{65}{105}$ = ________

21) $\frac{5600}{700}$ = ________ 22) $\frac{398}{40}$ = ________ 23) $\frac{8}{32}$ = ________ 24) $\frac{248}{44}$ = ________

25) $\frac{20}{32}$ = ________ 26) $\frac{54}{207}$ = ________ 27) $\frac{760}{152}$ = ________ 28) $\frac{18}{153}$ = ________

29) $\frac{232}{40}$ = ________ 30) $\frac{4}{12}$ = ________ 31) $\frac{1200}{240}$ = ________ 32) $\frac{375}{75}$ = ________

PP) Simplify the fractions.

1) $\frac{54}{10}$ = ______ 2) $\frac{214}{38}$ = ______ 3) $\frac{72}{126}$ = ______ 4) $\frac{483}{161}$ = ______

5) $\frac{816}{200}$ = ______ 6) $\frac{438}{96}$ = ______ 7) $\frac{153}{36}$ = ______ 8) $\frac{26}{60}$ = ______

9) $\frac{3696}{700}$ = ______ 10) $\frac{336}{48}$ = ______ 11) $\frac{80}{40}$ = ______ 12) $\frac{6}{42}$ = ______

13) $\frac{360}{85}$ = ______ 14) $\frac{130}{26}$ = ______ 15) $\frac{148}{44}$ = ______ 16) $\frac{791}{140}$ = ______

17) $\frac{324}{108}$ = ______ 18) $\frac{952}{96}$ = ______ 19) $\frac{228}{240}$ = ______ 20) $\frac{388}{88}$ = ______

21) $\frac{273}{91}$ = ______ 22) $\frac{25}{35}$ = ______ 23) $\frac{60}{72}$ = ______ 24) $\frac{539}{210}$ = ______

25) $\frac{28}{32}$ = ______ 26) $\frac{597}{120}$ = ______ 27) $\frac{96}{16}$ = ______ 28) $\frac{484}{96}$ = ______

29) $\frac{12}{20}$ = ______ 30) $\frac{1000}{112}$ = ______ 31) $\frac{55}{75}$ = ______ 32) $\frac{170}{18}$ = ______

QQ) Simplify the fractions.

1) $\frac{378}{189}$ = ________

2) $\frac{84}{140}$ = ________

3) $\frac{3150}{450}$ = ________

4) $\frac{50}{10}$ = ________

5) $\frac{16}{96}$ = ________

6) $\frac{56}{12}$ = ________

7) $\frac{342}{135}$ = ________

8) $\frac{245}{35}$ = ________

9) $\frac{1350}{225}$ = ________

10) $\frac{231}{77}$ = ________

11) $\frac{3}{39}$ = ________

12) $\frac{85}{120}$ = ________

13) $\frac{171}{57}$ = ________

14) $\frac{364}{56}$ = ________

15) $\frac{256}{480}$ = ________

16) $\frac{183}{30}$ = ________

17) $\frac{2380}{420}$ = ________

18) $\frac{144}{16}$ = ________

19) $\frac{268}{44}$ = ________

20) $\frac{18}{24}$ = ________

21) $\frac{189}{21}$ = ________

22) $\frac{196}{28}$ = ________

23) $\frac{544}{80}$ = ________

24) $\frac{1440}{160}$ = ________

25) $\frac{546}{108}$ = ________

26) $\frac{609}{63}$ = ________

27) $\frac{24}{60}$ = ________

28) $\frac{84}{225}$ = ________

29) $\frac{1272}{400}$ = ________

30) $\frac{546}{91}$ = ________

31) $\frac{450}{207}$ = ________

32) $\frac{66}{12}$ = ________

RR) Simplify the fractions.

1) $\frac{8}{136}$ = ______ 2) $\frac{738}{138}$ = ______ 3) $\frac{240}{120}$ = ______ 4) $\frac{168}{32}$ = ______

5) $\frac{48}{15}$ = ______ 6) $\frac{168}{24}$ = ______ 7) $\frac{20}{28}$ = ______ 8) $\frac{696}{150}$ = ______

9) $\frac{1920}{320}$ = ______ 10) $\frac{969}{150}$ = ______ 11) $\frac{48}{16}$ = ______ 12) $\frac{42}{77}$ = ______

13) $\frac{1050}{150}$ = ______ 14) $\frac{1368}{152}$ = ______ 15) $\frac{117}{180}$ = ______ 16) $\frac{378}{63}$ = ______

17) $\frac{48}{24}$ = ______ 18) $\frac{504}{56}$ = ______ 19) $\frac{154}{22}$ = ______ 20) $\frac{18}{90}$ = ______

21) $\frac{44}{64}$ = ______ 22) $\frac{1449}{153}$ = ______ 23) $\frac{240}{80}$ = ______ 24) $\frac{1288}{161}$ = ______

25) $\frac{632}{192}$ = ______ 26) $\frac{450}{50}$ = ______ 27) $\frac{112}{133}$ = ______ 28) $\frac{8}{12}$ = ______

29) $\frac{4}{18}$ = ______ 30) $\frac{68}{100}$ = ______ 31) $\frac{10}{26}$ = ______ 32) $\frac{4986}{540}$ = ______

SS) Simplify the fractions.

1) $\frac{745}{85}$ = ________ 2) $\frac{1505}{525}$ = ________ 3) $\frac{560}{96}$ = ________ 4) $\frac{152}{76}$ = ________

5) $\frac{700}{100}$ = ________ 6) $\frac{114}{54}$ = ________ 7) $\frac{32}{50}$ = ________ 8) $\frac{196}{49}$ = ________

9) $\frac{12}{30}$ = ________ 10) $\frac{198}{48}$ = ________ 11) $\frac{2781}{360}$ = ________ 12) $\frac{1096}{112}$ = ________

13) $\frac{441}{48}$ = ________ 14) $\frac{180}{30}$ = ________ 15) $\frac{440}{104}$ = ________ 16) $\frac{528}{66}$ = ________

17) $\frac{162}{54}$ = ________ 18) $\frac{432}{48}$ = ________ 19) $\frac{405}{125}$ = ________ 20) $\frac{1125}{225}$ = ________

21) $\frac{42}{138}$ = ________ 22) $\frac{54}{120}$ = ________ 23) $\frac{18}{126}$ = ________ 24) $\frac{900}{300}$ = ________

25) $\frac{15}{36}$ = ________ 26) $\frac{1656}{300}$ = ________ 27) $\frac{1080}{120}$ = ________ 28) $\frac{8}{28}$ = ________

29) $\frac{1605}{180}$ = ________ 30) $\frac{56}{126}$ = ________ 31) $\frac{112}{14}$ = ________ 32) $\frac{12}{18}$ = ________

TT) Simplify the fractions.

1) $\frac{18}{81}$ = ________ 2) $\frac{175}{35}$ = ________ 3) $\frac{256}{32}$ = ________ 4) $\frac{10}{70}$ = ________

5) $\frac{140}{420}$ = ________ 6) $\frac{54}{63}$ = ________ 7) $\frac{18}{9}$ = ________ 8) $\frac{810}{90}$ = ________

9) $\frac{40}{75}$ = ________ 10) $\frac{644}{91}$ = ________ 11) $\frac{300}{75}$ = ________ 12) $\frac{87}{90}$ = ________

13) $\frac{12}{68}$ = ________ 14) $\frac{40}{10}$ = ________ 15) $\frac{12}{69}$ = ________ 16) $\frac{1360}{480}$ = ________

17) $\frac{7}{28}$ = ________ 18) $\frac{182}{20}$ = ________ 19) $\frac{150}{30}$ = ________ 20) $\frac{30}{10}$ = ________

21) $\frac{450}{70}$ = ________ 22) $\frac{1400}{154}$ = ________ 23) $\frac{9}{27}$ = ________ 24) $\frac{882}{126}$ = ________

25) $\frac{90}{117}$ = ________ 26) $\frac{324}{81}$ = ________ 27) $\frac{840}{168}$ = ________ 28) $\frac{195}{33}$ = ________

29) $\frac{894}{90}$ = ________ 30) $\frac{252}{675}$ = ________ 31) $\frac{1016}{152}$ = ________ 32) $\frac{1440}{240}$ = ________

UU) Simplify the fractions.

1) $\frac{900}{180}$ = ______ 2) $\frac{222}{60}$ = ______ 3) $\frac{567}{189}$ = ______ 4) $\frac{24}{32}$ = ______

5) $\frac{320}{100}$ = ______ 6) $\frac{225}{45}$ = ______ 7) $\frac{1152}{128}$ = ______ 8) $\frac{270}{30}$ = ______

9) $\frac{480}{96}$ = ______ 10) $\frac{50}{150}$ = ______ 11) $\frac{30}{55}$ = ______ 12) $\frac{420}{105}$ = ______

13) $\frac{264}{44}$ = ______ 14) $\frac{92}{100}$ = ______ 15) $\frac{84}{42}$ = ______ 16) $\frac{32}{48}$ = ______

17) $\frac{40}{80}$ = ______ 18) $\frac{2}{4}$ = ______ 19) $\frac{453}{48}$ = ______ 20) $\frac{441}{81}$ = ______

21) $\frac{8}{32}$ = ______ 22) $\frac{150}{16}$ = ______ 23) $\frac{2400}{300}$ = ______ 24) $\frac{16}{20}$ = ______

25) $\frac{162}{57}$ = ______ 26) $\frac{2070}{360}$ = ______ 27) $\frac{816}{102}$ = ______ 28) $\frac{88}{100}$ = ______

29) $\frac{480}{80}$ = ______ 30) $\frac{18}{27}$ = ______ 31) $\frac{270}{108}$ = ______ 32) $\frac{4270}{500}$ = ______

VV) Simplify the fractions.

1) $\frac{1440}{360}$ = ______
2) $\frac{1680}{240}$ = ______
3) $\frac{45}{81}$ = ______
4) $\frac{960}{132}$ = ______

5) $\frac{384}{96}$ = ______
6) $\frac{7}{42}$ = ______
7) $\frac{33}{36}$ = ______
8) $\frac{72}{144}$ = ______

9) $\frac{120}{150}$ = ______
10) $\frac{1170}{360}$ = ______
11) $\frac{6}{21}$ = ______
12) $\frac{20}{64}$ = ______

13) $\frac{708}{114}$ = ______
14) $\frac{133}{14}$ = ______
15) $\frac{144}{40}$ = ______
16) $\frac{320}{85}$ = ______

17) $\frac{414}{69}$ = ______
18) $\frac{528}{90}$ = ______
19) $\frac{940}{100}$ = ______
20) $\frac{576}{72}$ = ______

21) $\frac{532}{80}$ = ______
22) $\frac{847}{98}$ = ______
23) $\frac{345}{500}$ = ______
24) $\frac{147}{63}$ = ______

25) $\frac{4}{48}$ = ______
26) $\frac{30}{6}$ = ______
27) $\frac{1152}{144}$ = ______
28) $\frac{104}{26}$ = ______

29) $\frac{738}{99}$ = ______
30) $\frac{70}{98}$ = ______
31) $\frac{8}{16}$ = ______
32) $\frac{8}{28}$ = ______

WW) Simplify the fractions.

1) $\frac{288}{36}$ = ______ 2) $\frac{6}{34}$ = ______ 3) $\frac{18}{48}$ = ______ 4) $\frac{98}{105}$ = ______

5) $\frac{150}{375}$ = ______ 6) $\frac{666}{72}$ = ______ 7) $\frac{308}{49}$ = ______ 8) $\frac{16}{480}$ = ______

9) $\frac{40}{44}$ = ______ 10) $\frac{102}{15}$ = ______ 11) $\frac{38}{60}$ = ______ 12) $\frac{400}{80}$ = ______

13) $\frac{5}{115}$ = ______ 14) $\frac{1071}{198}$ = ______ 15) $\frac{9}{189}$ = ______ 16) $\frac{152}{38}$ = ______

17) $\frac{228}{54}$ = ______ 18) $\frac{450}{150}$ = ______ 19) $\frac{91}{168}$ = ______ 20) $\frac{54}{27}$ = ______

21) $\frac{96}{112}$ = ______ 22) $\frac{840}{240}$ = ______ 23) $\frac{12}{51}$ = ______ 24) $\frac{84}{360}$ = ______

25) $\frac{220}{55}$ = ______ 26) $\frac{266}{28}$ = ______ 27) $\frac{56}{28}$ = ______ 28) $\frac{144}{150}$ = ______

29) $\frac{666}{84}$ = ______ 30) $\frac{567}{63}$ = ______ 31) $\frac{63}{112}$ = ______ 32) $\frac{14}{38}$ = ______

XX) Simplify the fractions.

1) $\frac{561}{66}$ = ________

2) $\frac{296}{88}$ = ________

3) $\frac{175}{60}$ = ________

4) $\frac{342}{450}$ = ________

5) $\frac{84}{126}$ = ________

6) $\frac{357}{51}$ = ________

7) $\frac{1056}{150}$ = ________

8) $\frac{96}{240}$ = ________

9) $\frac{36}{207}$ = ________

10) $\frac{21}{27}$ = ________

11) $\frac{440}{480}$ = ________

12) $\frac{420}{48}$ = ________

13) $\frac{6680}{800}$ = ________

14) $\frac{91}{140}$ = ________

15) $\frac{150}{30}$ = ________

16) $\frac{486}{54}$ = ________

17) $\frac{133}{21}$ = ________

18) $\frac{28}{60}$ = ________

19) $\frac{117}{360}$ = ________

20) $\frac{90}{144}$ = ________

21) $\frac{232}{240}$ = ________

22) $\frac{567}{135}$ = ________

23) $\frac{112}{56}$ = ________

24) $\frac{9}{36}$ = ________

25) $\frac{600}{150}$ = ________

26) $\frac{300}{100}$ = ________

27) $\frac{128}{144}$ = ________

28) $\frac{24}{48}$ = ________

29) $\frac{1392}{150}$ = ________

30) $\frac{200}{375}$ = ________

31) $\frac{610}{105}$ = ________

32) $\frac{16}{40}$ = ________

A) Simplify the fractions.

1) $\frac{35}{56} = \frac{5}{8}$

2) $\frac{8}{24} = \frac{1}{3}$

3) $\frac{21}{56} = \frac{3}{8}$

4) $\frac{9}{36} = \frac{1}{4}$

5) $\frac{2}{10} = \frac{1}{5}$

6) $\frac{14}{42} = \frac{1}{3}$

7) $\frac{16}{20} = \frac{4}{5}$

8) $\frac{6}{8} = \frac{3}{4}$

9) $\frac{9}{72} = \frac{1}{8}$

10) $\frac{15}{30} = \frac{1}{2}$

11) $\frac{4}{6} = \frac{2}{3}$

12) $\frac{63}{72} = \frac{7}{8}$

13) $\frac{21}{35} = \frac{3}{5}$

14) $\frac{12}{18} = \frac{2}{3}$

15) $\frac{4}{24} = \frac{1}{6}$

16) $\frac{14}{21} = \frac{2}{3}$

17) $\frac{4}{12} = \frac{1}{3}$

18) $\frac{20}{40} = \frac{1}{2}$

19) $\frac{12}{15} = \frac{4}{5}$

20) $\frac{14}{28} = \frac{1}{2}$

21) $\frac{27}{45} = \frac{3}{5}$

22) $\frac{3}{9} = \frac{1}{3}$

23) $\frac{9}{54} = \frac{1}{6}$

24) $\frac{2}{8} = \frac{1}{4}$

25) $\frac{2}{16} = \frac{1}{8}$

26) $\frac{3}{24} = \frac{1}{8}$

27) $\frac{3}{18} = \frac{1}{6}$

28) $\frac{20}{25} = \frac{4}{5}$

29) $\frac{5}{15} = \frac{1}{3}$

30) $\frac{6}{24} = \frac{1}{4}$

31) $\frac{8}{16} = \frac{1}{2}$

32) $\frac{18}{24} = \frac{3}{4}$

B) Simplify the fractions.

1) $\frac{3}{15} = \frac{1}{5}$ ______ 2) $\frac{9}{12} = \frac{3}{4}$ ______ 3) $\frac{10}{25} = \frac{2}{5}$ ______ 4) $\frac{12}{32} = \frac{3}{8}$ ______

5) $\frac{9}{54} = \frac{1}{6}$ ______ 6) $\frac{6}{24} = \frac{1}{4}$ ______ 7) $\frac{8}{12} = \frac{2}{3}$ ______ 8) $\frac{18}{27} = \frac{2}{3}$ ______

9) $\frac{18}{36} = \frac{1}{2}$ ______ 10) $\frac{16}{40} = \frac{2}{5}$ ______ 11) $\frac{4}{16} = \frac{1}{4}$ ______ 12) $\frac{15}{30} = \frac{1}{2}$ ______

13) $\frac{3}{24} = \frac{1}{8}$ ______ 14) $\frac{4}{12} = \frac{1}{3}$ ______ 15) $\frac{8}{16} = \frac{1}{2}$ ______ 16) $\frac{24}{36} = \frac{2}{3}$ ______

17) $\frac{5}{15} = \frac{1}{3}$ ______ 18) $\frac{6}{36} = \frac{1}{6}$ ______ 19) $\frac{14}{35} = \frac{2}{5}$ ______ 20) $\frac{5}{20} = \frac{1}{4}$ ______

21) $\frac{20}{32} = \frac{5}{8}$ ______ 22) $\frac{6}{16} = \frac{3}{8}$ ______ 23) $\frac{3}{12} = \frac{1}{4}$ ______ 24) $\frac{27}{72} = \frac{3}{8}$ ______

25) $\frac{10}{15} = \frac{2}{3}$ ______ 26) $\frac{32}{40} = \frac{4}{5}$ ______ 27) $\frac{10}{30} = \frac{1}{3}$ ______ 28) $\frac{6}{18} = \frac{1}{3}$ ______

29) $\frac{12}{16} = \frac{3}{4}$ ______ 30) $\frac{18}{30} = \frac{3}{5}$ ______ 31) $\frac{27}{45} = \frac{3}{5}$ ______ 32) $\frac{9}{24} = \frac{3}{8}$ ______

C) Simplify the fractions.

1) $\frac{30}{40} = \frac{3}{4}$ ______

2) $\frac{16}{24} = \frac{2}{3}$ ______

3) $\frac{9}{12} = \frac{3}{4}$ ______

4) $\frac{4}{12} = \frac{1}{3}$ ______

5) $\frac{27}{45} = \frac{3}{5}$ ______

6) $\frac{24}{36} = \frac{2}{3}$ ______

7) $\frac{2}{16} = \frac{1}{8}$ ______

8) $\frac{2}{8} = \frac{1}{4}$ ______

9) $\frac{8}{24} = \frac{1}{3}$ ______

10) $\frac{18}{24} = \frac{3}{4}$ ______

11) $\frac{40}{64} = \frac{5}{8}$ ______

12) $\frac{9}{18} = \frac{1}{2}$ ______

13) $\frac{16}{40} = \frac{2}{5}$ ______

14) $\frac{9}{27} = \frac{1}{3}$ ______

15) $\frac{6}{8} = \frac{3}{4}$ ______

16) $\frac{16}{32} = \frac{1}{2}$ ______

17) $\frac{9}{54} = \frac{1}{6}$ ______

18) $\frac{24}{40} = \frac{3}{5}$ ______

19) $\frac{12}{24} = \frac{1}{2}$ ______

20) $\frac{9}{15} = \frac{3}{5}$ ______

21) $\frac{21}{24} = \frac{7}{8}$ ______

22) $\frac{8}{40} = \frac{1}{5}$ ______

23) $\frac{24}{64} = \frac{3}{8}$ ______

24) $\frac{9}{36} = \frac{1}{4}$ ______

25) $\frac{2}{6} = \frac{1}{3}$ ______

26) $\frac{40}{48} = \frac{5}{6}$ ______

27) $\frac{4}{10} = \frac{2}{5}$ ______

28) $\frac{12}{18} = \frac{2}{3}$ ______

29) $\frac{18}{48} = \frac{3}{8}$ ______

30) $\frac{8}{16} = \frac{1}{2}$ ______

31) $\frac{4}{6} = \frac{2}{3}$ ______

32) $\frac{10}{30} = \frac{1}{3}$ ______

D) Simplify the fractions.

1) $\frac{10}{20} = \frac{1}{2}$

2) $\frac{5}{15} = \frac{1}{3}$

3) $\frac{12}{24} = \frac{1}{2}$

4) $\frac{2}{12} = \frac{1}{6}$

5) $\frac{6}{8} = \frac{3}{4}$

6) $\frac{8}{12} = \frac{2}{3}$

7) $\frac{10}{25} = \frac{2}{5}$

8) $\frac{15}{40} = \frac{3}{8}$

9) $\frac{27}{36} = \frac{3}{4}$

10) $\frac{8}{10} = \frac{4}{5}$

11) $\frac{8}{64} = \frac{1}{8}$

12) $\frac{7}{42} = \frac{1}{6}$

13) $\frac{9}{12} = \frac{3}{4}$

14) $\frac{28}{35} = \frac{4}{5}$

15) $\frac{6}{18} = \frac{1}{3}$

16) $\frac{36}{72} = \frac{1}{2}$

17) $\frac{8}{24} = \frac{1}{3}$

18) $\frac{8}{40} = \frac{1}{5}$

19) $\frac{42}{56} = \frac{3}{4}$

20) $\frac{15}{18} = \frac{5}{6}$

21) $\frac{18}{36} = \frac{1}{2}$

22) $\frac{9}{27} = \frac{1}{3}$

23) $\frac{6}{12} = \frac{1}{2}$

24) $\frac{18}{72} = \frac{1}{4}$

25) $\frac{24}{48} = \frac{1}{2}$

26) $\frac{20}{25} = \frac{4}{5}$

27) $\frac{30}{36} = \frac{5}{6}$

28) $\frac{4}{12} = \frac{1}{3}$

29) $\frac{8}{16} = \frac{1}{2}$

30) $\frac{16}{40} = \frac{2}{5}$

31) $\frac{4}{16} = \frac{1}{4}$

32) $\frac{35}{56} = \frac{5}{8}$

E) Simplify the fractions.

1) $\frac{2}{12} = \frac{1}{6}$ ______

2) $\frac{20}{32} = \frac{5}{8}$ ______

3) $\frac{9}{15} = \frac{3}{5}$ ______

4) $\frac{18}{27} = \frac{2}{3}$ ______

5) $\frac{6}{48} = \frac{1}{8}$ ______

6) $\frac{3}{15} = \frac{1}{5}$ ______

7) $\frac{10}{15} = \frac{2}{3}$ ______

8) $\frac{36}{54} = \frac{2}{3}$ ______

9) $\frac{4}{8} = \frac{1}{2}$ ______

10) $\frac{3}{9} = \frac{1}{3}$ ______

11) $\frac{4}{10} = \frac{2}{5}$ ______

12) $\frac{24}{64} = \frac{3}{8}$ ______

13) $\frac{6}{12} = \frac{1}{2}$ ______

14) $\frac{6}{36} = \frac{1}{6}$ ______

15) $\frac{16}{24} = \frac{2}{3}$ ______

16) $\frac{21}{35} = \frac{3}{5}$ ______

17) $\frac{27}{72} = \frac{3}{8}$ ______

18) $\frac{18}{24} = \frac{3}{4}$ ______

19) $\frac{24}{36} = \frac{2}{3}$ ______

20) $\frac{4}{6} = \frac{2}{3}$ ______

21) $\frac{15}{20} = \frac{3}{4}$ ______

22) $\frac{32}{48} = \frac{2}{3}$ ______

23) $\frac{14}{56} = \frac{1}{4}$ ______

24) $\frac{10}{25} = \frac{2}{5}$ ______

25) $\frac{45}{54} = \frac{5}{6}$ ______

26) $\frac{14}{21} = \frac{2}{3}$ ______

27) $\frac{15}{25} = \frac{3}{5}$ ______

28) $\frac{18}{72} = \frac{1}{4}$ ______

29) $\frac{24}{32} = \frac{3}{4}$ ______

30) $\frac{25}{30} = \frac{5}{6}$ ______

31) $\frac{5}{15} = \frac{1}{3}$ ______

32) $\frac{4}{16} = \frac{1}{4}$ ______

F) Simplify the fractions.

1) $\frac{12}{18} = \frac{2}{3}$

2) $\frac{15}{20} = \frac{3}{4}$

3) $\frac{24}{40} = \frac{3}{5}$

4) $\frac{16}{64} = \frac{1}{4}$

5) $\frac{24}{32} = \frac{3}{4}$

6) $\frac{3}{9} = \frac{1}{3}$

7) $\frac{10}{12} = \frac{5}{6}$

8) $\frac{21}{42} = \frac{1}{2}$

9) $\frac{28}{56} = \frac{1}{2}$

10) $\frac{10}{20} = \frac{1}{2}$

11) $\frac{8}{24} = \frac{1}{3}$

12) $\frac{2}{10} = \frac{1}{5}$

13) $\frac{21}{35} = \frac{3}{5}$

14) $\frac{5}{40} = \frac{1}{8}$

15) $\frac{8}{12} = \frac{2}{3}$

16) $\frac{7}{28} = \frac{1}{4}$

17) $\frac{16}{24} = \frac{2}{3}$

18) $\frac{27}{36} = \frac{3}{4}$

19) $\frac{4}{16} = \frac{1}{4}$

20) $\frac{16}{48} = \frac{1}{3}$

21) $\frac{7}{21} = \frac{1}{3}$

22) $\frac{3}{15} = \frac{1}{5}$

23) $\frac{10}{15} = \frac{2}{3}$

24) $\frac{63}{72} = \frac{7}{8}$

25) $\frac{12}{16} = \frac{3}{4}$

26) $\frac{3}{18} = \frac{1}{6}$

27) $\frac{12}{20} = \frac{3}{5}$

28) $\frac{9}{27} = \frac{1}{3}$

29) $\frac{16}{32} = \frac{1}{2}$

30) $\frac{27}{45} = \frac{3}{5}$

31) $\frac{7}{42} = \frac{1}{6}$

32) $\frac{20}{40} = \frac{1}{2}$

G) Simplify the fractions.

1) $\frac{2}{6} = \frac{1}{3}$ ______

2) $\frac{10}{20} = \frac{1}{2}$ ______

3) $\frac{14}{35} = \frac{2}{5}$ ______

4) $\frac{6}{18} = \frac{1}{3}$ ______

5) $\frac{6}{30} = \frac{1}{5}$ ______

6) $\frac{16}{32} = \frac{1}{2}$ ______

7) $\frac{8}{24} = \frac{1}{3}$ ______

8) $\frac{8}{64} = \frac{1}{8}$ ______

9) $\frac{10}{15} = \frac{2}{3}$ ______

10) $\frac{4}{12} = \frac{1}{3}$ ______

11) $\frac{18}{24} = \frac{3}{4}$ ______

12) $\frac{6}{9} = \frac{2}{3}$ ______

13) $\frac{12}{30} = \frac{2}{5}$ ______

14) $\frac{54}{72} = \frac{3}{4}$ ______

15) $\frac{3}{12} = \frac{1}{4}$ ______

16) $\frac{8}{12} = \frac{2}{3}$ ______

17) $\frac{5}{20} = \frac{1}{4}$ ______

18) $\frac{7}{42} = \frac{1}{6}$ ______

19) $\frac{5}{25} = \frac{1}{5}$ ______

20) $\frac{12}{18} = \frac{2}{3}$ ______

21) $\frac{6}{48} = \frac{1}{8}$ ______

22) $\frac{15}{20} = \frac{3}{4}$ ______

23) $\frac{16}{20} = \frac{4}{5}$ ______

24) $\frac{8}{48} = \frac{1}{6}$ ______

25) $\frac{14}{21} = \frac{2}{3}$ ______

26) $\frac{15}{40} = \frac{3}{8}$ ______

27) $\frac{9}{12} = \frac{3}{4}$ ______

28) $\frac{7}{35} = \frac{1}{5}$ ______

29) $\frac{9}{18} = \frac{1}{2}$ ______

30) $\frac{5}{15} = \frac{1}{3}$ ______

31) $\frac{4}{32} = \frac{1}{8}$ ______

32) $\frac{2}{8} = \frac{1}{4}$ ______

H) Simplify the fractions.

1) $\frac{15}{40} = \frac{3}{8}$ ______

2) $\frac{2}{12} = \frac{1}{6}$ ______

3) $\frac{9}{36} = \frac{1}{4}$ ______

4) $\frac{18}{27} = \frac{2}{3}$ ______

5) $\frac{32}{48} = \frac{2}{3}$ ______

6) $\frac{21}{28} = \frac{3}{4}$ ______

7) $\frac{10}{15} = \frac{2}{3}$ ______

8) $\frac{28}{32} = \frac{7}{8}$ ______

9) $\frac{4}{20} = \frac{1}{5}$ ______

10) $\frac{20}{30} = \frac{2}{3}$ ______

11) $\frac{7}{35} = \frac{1}{5}$ ______

12) $\frac{8}{32} = \frac{1}{4}$ ______

13) $\frac{14}{21} = \frac{2}{3}$ ______

14) $\frac{35}{40} = \frac{7}{8}$ ______

15) $\frac{40}{48} = \frac{5}{6}$ ______

16) $\frac{14}{16} = \frac{7}{8}$ ______

17) $\frac{4}{16} = \frac{1}{4}$ ______

18) $\frac{8}{24} = \frac{1}{3}$ ______

19) $\frac{2}{10} = \frac{1}{5}$ ______

20) $\frac{15}{20} = \frac{3}{4}$ ______

21) $\frac{9}{72} = \frac{1}{8}$ ______

22) $\frac{5}{15} = \frac{1}{3}$ ______

23) $\frac{12}{30} = \frac{2}{5}$ ______

24) $\frac{14}{42} = \frac{1}{3}$ ______

25) $\frac{15}{30} = \frac{1}{2}$ ______

26) $\frac{12}{24} = \frac{1}{2}$ ______

27) $\frac{42}{48} = \frac{7}{8}$ ______

28) $\frac{6}{15} = \frac{2}{5}$ ______

29) $\frac{56}{64} = \frac{7}{8}$ ______

30) $\frac{16}{24} = \frac{2}{3}$ ______

31) $\frac{15}{25} = \frac{3}{5}$ ______

32) $\frac{2}{6} = \frac{1}{3}$ ______

I) Simplify the fractions.

1) $\frac{7}{21} = \frac{1}{3}$

2) $\frac{5}{25} = \frac{1}{5}$

3) $\frac{28}{32} = \frac{7}{8}$

4) $\frac{8}{48} = \frac{1}{6}$

5) $\frac{18}{30} = \frac{3}{5}$

6) $\frac{6}{8} = \frac{3}{4}$

7) $\frac{45}{72} = \frac{5}{8}$

8) $\frac{3}{9} = \frac{1}{3}$

9) $\frac{7}{42} = \frac{1}{6}$

10) $\frac{10}{15} = \frac{2}{3}$

11) $\frac{21}{35} = \frac{3}{5}$

12) $\frac{8}{24} = \frac{1}{3}$

13) $\frac{14}{16} = \frac{7}{8}$

14) $\frac{6}{9} = \frac{2}{3}$

15) $\frac{8}{20} = \frac{2}{5}$

16) $\frac{15}{20} = \frac{3}{4}$

17) $\frac{24}{32} = \frac{3}{4}$

18) $\frac{10}{20} = \frac{1}{2}$

19) $\frac{20}{32} = \frac{5}{8}$

20) $\frac{4}{12} = \frac{1}{3}$

21) $\frac{18}{27} = \frac{2}{3}$

22) $\frac{8}{32} = \frac{1}{4}$

23) $\frac{24}{30} = \frac{4}{5}$

24) $\frac{35}{56} = \frac{5}{8}$

25) $\frac{10}{12} = \frac{5}{6}$

26) $\frac{6}{16} = \frac{3}{8}$

27) $\frac{20}{25} = \frac{4}{5}$

28) $\frac{4}{16} = \frac{1}{4}$

29) $\frac{6}{18} = \frac{1}{3}$

30) $\frac{8}{12} = \frac{2}{3}$

31) $\frac{27}{54} = \frac{1}{2}$

32) $\frac{2}{8} = \frac{1}{4}$

J) Simplify the fractions.

1) $\frac{1}{4} = \frac{1}{4}$

2) $\frac{4}{12} = \frac{1}{3}$

3) $\frac{10}{12} = \frac{5}{6}$

4) $\frac{14}{21} = \frac{2}{3}$

5) $\frac{12}{20} = \frac{3}{5}$

6) $\frac{12}{16} = \frac{3}{4}$

7) $\frac{18}{24} = \frac{3}{4}$

8) $\frac{18}{48} = \frac{3}{8}$

9) $\frac{16}{40} = \frac{2}{5}$

10) $\frac{12}{24} = \frac{1}{2}$

11) $\frac{6}{30} = \frac{1}{5}$

12) $\frac{4}{16} = \frac{1}{4}$

13) $\frac{10}{15} = \frac{2}{3}$

14) $\frac{7}{42} = \frac{1}{6}$

15) $\frac{12}{30} = \frac{2}{5}$

16) $\frac{5}{20} = \frac{1}{4}$

17) $\frac{6}{18} = \frac{1}{3}$

18) $\frac{6}{12} = \frac{1}{2}$

19) $\frac{2}{6} = \frac{1}{3}$

20) $\frac{8}{64} = \frac{1}{8}$

21) $\frac{32}{40} = \frac{4}{5}$

22) $\frac{10}{20} = \frac{1}{2}$

23) $\frac{15}{20} = \frac{3}{4}$

24) $\frac{10}{25} = \frac{2}{5}$

25) $\frac{27}{54} = \frac{1}{2}$

26) $\frac{4}{32} = \frac{1}{8}$

27) $\frac{7}{21} = \frac{1}{3}$

28) $\frac{8}{12} = \frac{2}{3}$

29) $\frac{8}{16} = \frac{1}{2}$

30) $\frac{24}{30} = \frac{4}{5}$

31) $\frac{36}{72} = \frac{1}{2}$

32) $\frac{6}{36} = \frac{1}{6}$

K) Simplify the fractions.

1) $\frac{162}{24} = 6\frac{3}{4}$

2) $\frac{75}{24} = 3\frac{1}{8}$

3) $\frac{6}{12} = \frac{1}{2}$

4) $\frac{300}{40} = 7\frac{1}{2}$

5) $\frac{82}{12} = 6\frac{5}{6}$

6) $\frac{6}{10} = \frac{3}{5}$

7) $\frac{174}{18} = 9\frac{2}{3}$

8) $\frac{186}{48} = 3\frac{7}{8}$

9) $\frac{66}{18} = 3\frac{2}{3}$

10) $\frac{224}{35} = 6\frac{2}{5}$

11) $\frac{140}{21} = 6\frac{2}{3}$

12) $\frac{165}{20} = 8\frac{1}{4}$

13) $\frac{140}{15} = 9\frac{1}{3}$

14) $\frac{12}{24} = \frac{1}{2}$

15) $\frac{30}{48} = \frac{5}{8}$

16) $\frac{280}{30} = 9\frac{1}{3}$

17) $\frac{85}{25} = 3\frac{2}{5}$

18) $\frac{304}{40} = 7\frac{3}{5}$

19) $\frac{26}{8} = 3\frac{1}{4}$

20) $\frac{333}{54} = 6\frac{1}{6}$

21) $\frac{8}{12} = \frac{2}{3}$

22) $\frac{376}{64} = 5\frac{7}{8}$

23) $\frac{20}{24} = \frac{5}{6}$

24) $\frac{48}{64} = \frac{3}{4}$

25) $\frac{84}{18} = 4\frac{2}{3}$

26) $\frac{3}{12} = \frac{1}{4}$

27) $\frac{138}{15} = 9\frac{1}{5}$

28) $\frac{90}{20} = 4\frac{1}{2}$

29) $\frac{352}{40} = 8\frac{4}{5}$

30) $\frac{51}{9} = 5\frac{2}{3}$

31) $\frac{32}{64} = \frac{1}{2}$

32) $\frac{16}{40} = \frac{2}{5}$

L) Simplify the fractions.

1) $\frac{216}{32} = 6\frac{3}{4}$

2) $\frac{204}{30} = 6\frac{4}{5}$

3) $\frac{21}{24} = \frac{7}{8}$

4) $\frac{116}{12} = 9\frac{2}{3}$

5) $\frac{32}{40} = \frac{4}{5}$

6) $\frac{8}{24} = \frac{1}{3}$

7) $\frac{42}{9} = 4\frac{2}{3}$

8) $\frac{15}{40} = \frac{3}{8}$

9) $\frac{75}{12} = 6\frac{1}{4}$

10) $\frac{544}{64} = 8\frac{1}{2}$

11) $\frac{82}{12} = 6\frac{5}{6}$

12) $\frac{128}{24} = 5\frac{1}{3}$

13) $\frac{204}{24} = 8\frac{1}{2}$

14) $\frac{7}{35} = \frac{1}{5}$

15) $\frac{145}{15} = 9\frac{2}{3}$

16) $\frac{168}{20} = 8\frac{2}{5}$

17) $\frac{20}{8} = 2\frac{1}{2}$

18) $\frac{224}{64} = 3\frac{1}{2}$

19) $\frac{450}{54} = 8\frac{1}{3}$

20) $\frac{8}{10} = \frac{4}{5}$

21) $\frac{7}{42} = \frac{1}{6}$

22) $\frac{3}{9} = \frac{1}{3}$

23) $\frac{520}{64} = 8\frac{1}{8}$

24) $\frac{21}{28} = \frac{3}{4}$

25) $\frac{81}{15} = 5\frac{2}{5}$

26) $\frac{4}{12} = \frac{1}{3}$

27) $\frac{108}{32} = 3\frac{3}{8}$

28) $\frac{16}{48} = \frac{1}{3}$

29) $\frac{306}{36} = 8\frac{1}{2}$

30) $\frac{9}{27} = \frac{1}{3}$

31) $\frac{21}{42} = \frac{1}{2}$

32) $\frac{4}{16} = \frac{1}{4}$

M) Simplify the fractions.

1) $\frac{55}{15} = 3\frac{2}{3}$

2) $\frac{231}{35} = 6\frac{3}{5}$

3) $\frac{32}{64} = \frac{1}{2}$

4) $\frac{18}{30} = \frac{3}{5}$

5) $\frac{52}{12} = 4\frac{1}{3}$

6) $\frac{3}{12} = \frac{1}{4}$

7) $\frac{9}{18} = \frac{1}{2}$

8) $\frac{16}{24} = \frac{2}{3}$

9) $\frac{128}{40} = 3\frac{1}{5}$

10) $\frac{273}{42} = 6\frac{1}{2}$

11) $\frac{455}{56} = 8\frac{1}{8}$

12) $\frac{5}{20} = \frac{1}{4}$

13) $\frac{6}{18} = \frac{1}{3}$

14) $\frac{16}{40} = \frac{2}{5}$

15) $\frac{2}{6} = \frac{1}{3}$

16) $\frac{16}{32} = \frac{1}{2}$

17) $\frac{6}{24} = \frac{1}{4}$

18) $\frac{10}{15} = \frac{2}{3}$

19) $\frac{114}{16} = 7\frac{1}{8}$

20) $\frac{91}{28} = 3\frac{1}{4}$

21) $\frac{119}{35} = 3\frac{2}{5}$

22) $\frac{315}{42} = 7\frac{1}{2}$

23) $\frac{35}{42} = \frac{5}{6}$

24) $\frac{12}{18} = \frac{2}{3}$

25) $\frac{511}{56} = 9\frac{1}{8}$

26) $\frac{114}{24} = 4\frac{3}{4}$

27) $\frac{22}{10} = 2\frac{1}{5}$

28) $\frac{4}{6} = \frac{2}{3}$

29) $\frac{2}{10} = \frac{1}{5}$

30) $\frac{138}{36} = 3\frac{5}{6}$

31) $\frac{8}{32} = \frac{1}{4}$

32) $\frac{222}{24} = 9\frac{1}{4}$

N) Simplify the fractions.

1) $\frac{21}{42} = \frac{1}{2}$

2) $\frac{333}{45} = 7\frac{2}{5}$

3) $\frac{21}{28} = \frac{3}{4}$

4) $\frac{560}{64} = 8\frac{3}{4}$

5) $\frac{8}{24} = \frac{1}{3}$

6) $\frac{2}{12} = \frac{1}{6}$

7) $\frac{28}{8} = 3\frac{1}{2}$

8) $\frac{12}{30} = \frac{2}{5}$

9) $\frac{172}{32} = 5\frac{3}{8}$

10) $\frac{46}{6} = 7\frac{2}{3}$

11) $\frac{8}{16} = \frac{1}{2}$

12) $\frac{7}{35} = \frac{1}{5}$

13) $\frac{24}{36} = \frac{2}{3}$

14) $\frac{91}{21} = 4\frac{1}{3}$

15) $\frac{12}{16} = \frac{3}{4}$

16) $\frac{312}{40} = 7\frac{4}{5}$

17) $\frac{207}{36} = 5\frac{3}{4}$

18) $\frac{147}{18} = 8\frac{1}{6}$

19) $\frac{7}{21} = \frac{1}{3}$

20) $\frac{408}{48} = 8\frac{1}{2}$

21) $\frac{145}{15} = 9\frac{2}{3}$

22) $\frac{6}{12} = \frac{1}{2}$

23) $\frac{75}{18} = 4\frac{1}{6}$

24) $\frac{150}{24} = 6\frac{1}{4}$

25) $\frac{36}{10} = 3\frac{3}{5}$

26) $\frac{9}{27} = \frac{1}{3}$

27) $\frac{140}{42} = 3\frac{1}{3}$

28) $\frac{84}{15} = 5\frac{3}{5}$

29) $\frac{161}{28} = 5\frac{3}{4}$

30) $\frac{28}{32} = \frac{7}{8}$

31) $\frac{8}{20} = \frac{2}{5}$

32) $\frac{252}{27} = 9\frac{1}{3}$

O) Simplify the fractions.

1) $\frac{2}{4} = \frac{1}{2}$

2) $\frac{4}{24} = \frac{1}{6}$

3) $\frac{8}{32} = \frac{1}{4}$

4) $\frac{21}{35} = \frac{3}{5}$

5) $\frac{230}{40} = 5\frac{3}{4}$

6) $\frac{168}{48} = 3\frac{1}{2}$

7) $\frac{21}{9} = 2\frac{1}{3}$

8) $\frac{84}{24} = 3\frac{1}{2}$

9) $\frac{21}{24} = \frac{7}{8}$

10) $\frac{196}{21} = 9\frac{1}{3}$

11) $\frac{30}{12} = 2\frac{1}{2}$

12) $\frac{6}{12} = \frac{1}{2}$

13) $\frac{8}{64} = \frac{1}{8}$

14) $\frac{182}{21} = 8\frac{2}{3}$

15) $\frac{4}{20} = \frac{1}{5}$

16) $\frac{69}{12} = 5\frac{3}{4}$

17) $\frac{264}{32} = 8\frac{1}{4}$

18) $\frac{6}{36} = \frac{1}{6}$

19) $\frac{64}{10} = 6\frac{2}{5}$

20) $\frac{16}{32} = \frac{1}{2}$

21) $\frac{9}{27} = \frac{1}{3}$

22) $\frac{165}{20} = 8\frac{1}{4}$

23) $\frac{132}{24} = 5\frac{1}{2}$

24) $\frac{65}{25} = 2\frac{3}{5}$

25) $\frac{2}{6} = \frac{1}{3}$

26) $\frac{15}{40} = \frac{3}{8}$

27) $\frac{15}{20} = \frac{3}{4}$

28) $\frac{20}{40} = \frac{1}{2}$

29) $\frac{58}{10} = 5\frac{4}{5}$

30) $\frac{140}{15} = 9\frac{1}{3}$

31) $\frac{45}{54} = \frac{5}{6}$

32) $\frac{12}{16} = \frac{3}{4}$

P) Simplify the fractions.

1) $\frac{10}{15} = \frac{2}{3}$

2) $\frac{2}{12} = \frac{1}{6}$

3) $\frac{285}{40} = 7\frac{1}{8}$

4) $\frac{10}{20} = \frac{1}{2}$

5) $\frac{64}{10} = 6\frac{2}{5}$

6) $\frac{189}{28} = 6\frac{3}{4}$

7) $\frac{87}{9} = 9\frac{2}{3}$

8) $\frac{220}{30} = 7\frac{1}{3}$

9) $\frac{35}{56} = \frac{5}{8}$

10) $\frac{49}{56} = \frac{7}{8}$

11) $\frac{114}{30} = 3\frac{4}{5}$

12) $\frac{144}{27} = 5\frac{1}{3}$

13) $\frac{44}{12} = 3\frac{2}{3}$

14) $\frac{126}{28} = 4\frac{1}{2}$

15) $\frac{69}{12} = 5\frac{3}{4}$

16) $\frac{28}{56} = \frac{1}{2}$

17) $\frac{14}{21} = \frac{2}{3}$

18) $\frac{108}{45} = 2\frac{2}{5}$

19) $\frac{35}{42} = \frac{5}{6}$

20) $\frac{154}{28} = 5\frac{1}{2}$

21) $\frac{4}{12} = \frac{1}{3}$

22) $\frac{82}{10} = 8\frac{1}{5}$

23) $\frac{165}{40} = 4\frac{1}{8}$

24) $\frac{138}{36} = 3\frac{5}{6}$

25) $\frac{27}{72} = \frac{3}{8}$

26) $\frac{165}{30} = 5\frac{1}{2}$

27) $\frac{171}{27} = 6\frac{1}{3}$

28) $\frac{329}{35} = 9\frac{2}{5}$

29) $\frac{54}{8} = 6\frac{3}{4}$

30) $\frac{132}{18} = 7\frac{1}{3}$

31) $\frac{21}{28} = \frac{3}{4}$

32) $\frac{24}{48} = \frac{1}{2}$

Q) Simplify the fractions.

1) $\frac{6}{18} = \frac{1}{3}$

2) $\frac{12}{16} = \frac{3}{4}$

3) $\frac{16}{40} = \frac{2}{5}$

4) $\frac{110}{20} = 5\frac{1}{2}$

5) $\frac{10}{16} = \frac{5}{8}$

6) $\frac{105}{30} = 3\frac{1}{2}$

7) $\frac{12}{18} = \frac{2}{3}$

8) $\frac{276}{32} = 8\frac{5}{8}$

9) $\frac{198}{36} = 5\frac{1}{2}$

10) $\frac{36}{45} = \frac{4}{5}$

11) $\frac{51}{9} = 5\frac{2}{3}$

12) $\frac{30}{36} = \frac{5}{6}$

13) $\frac{147}{28} = 5\frac{1}{4}$

14) $\frac{48}{18} = 2\frac{2}{3}$

15) $\frac{4}{20} = \frac{1}{5}$

16) $\frac{171}{18} = 9\frac{1}{2}$

17) $\frac{212}{32} = 6\frac{5}{8}$

18) $\frac{7}{21} = \frac{1}{3}$

19) $\frac{8}{20} = \frac{2}{5}$

20) $\frac{6}{36} = \frac{1}{6}$

21) $\frac{93}{12} = 7\frac{3}{4}$

22) $\frac{416}{64} = 6\frac{1}{2}$

23) $\frac{497}{56} = 8\frac{7}{8}$

24) $\frac{69}{15} = 4\frac{3}{5}$

25) $\frac{126}{36} = 3\frac{1}{2}$

26) $\frac{128}{48} = 2\frac{2}{3}$

27) $\frac{20}{32} = \frac{5}{8}$

28) $\frac{99}{12} = 8\frac{1}{4}$

29) $\frac{28}{35} = \frac{4}{5}$

30) $\frac{8}{24} = \frac{1}{3}$

31) $\frac{16}{20} = \frac{4}{5}$

32) $\frac{18}{54} = \frac{1}{3}$

R) Simplify the fractions.

1) $\frac{28}{12} = 2\frac{1}{3}$

2) $\frac{6}{8} = \frac{3}{4}$

3) $\frac{423}{72} = 5\frac{7}{8}$

4) $\frac{16}{20} = \frac{4}{5}$

5) $\frac{12}{16} = \frac{3}{4}$

6) $\frac{420}{56} = 7\frac{1}{2}$

7) $\frac{450}{54} = 8\frac{1}{3}$

8) $\frac{12}{18} = \frac{2}{3}$

9) $\frac{224}{42} = 5\frac{1}{3}$

10) $\frac{64}{24} = 2\frac{2}{3}$

11) $\frac{184}{32} = 5\frac{3}{4}$

12) $\frac{350}{56} = 6\frac{1}{4}$

13) $\frac{133}{35} = 3\frac{4}{5}$

14) $\frac{336}{40} = 8\frac{2}{5}$

15) $\frac{20}{40} = \frac{1}{2}$

16) $\frac{16}{32} = \frac{1}{2}$

17) $\frac{165}{30} = 5\frac{1}{2}$

18) $\frac{171}{27} = 6\frac{1}{3}$

19) $\frac{10}{30} = \frac{1}{3}$

20) $\frac{126}{36} = 3\frac{1}{2}$

21) $\frac{18}{45} = \frac{2}{5}$

22) $\frac{9}{27} = \frac{1}{3}$

23) $\frac{4}{12} = \frac{1}{3}$

24) $\frac{522}{72} = 7\frac{1}{4}$

25) $\frac{8}{16} = \frac{1}{2}$

26) $\frac{24}{48} = \frac{1}{2}$

27) $\frac{12}{20} = \frac{3}{5}$

28) $\frac{39}{9} = 4\frac{1}{3}$

29) $\frac{132}{24} = 5\frac{1}{2}$

30) $\frac{2}{8} = \frac{1}{4}$

31) $\frac{21}{42} = \frac{1}{2}$

32) $\frac{62}{10} = 6\frac{1}{5}$

S) Simplify the fractions.

1) $\frac{23}{3} = 7\frac{2}{3}$

2) $\frac{8}{12} = \frac{2}{3}$

3) $\frac{9}{12} = \frac{3}{4}$

4) $\frac{15}{25} = \frac{3}{5}$

5) $\frac{12}{24} = \frac{1}{2}$

6) $\frac{30}{40} = \frac{3}{4}$

7) $\frac{2}{8} = \frac{1}{4}$

8) $\frac{222}{36} = 6\frac{1}{6}$

9) $\frac{138}{30} = 4\frac{3}{5}$

10) $\frac{99}{27} = 3\frac{2}{3}$

11) $\frac{7}{21} = \frac{1}{3}$

12) $\frac{198}{54} = 3\frac{2}{3}$

13) $\frac{16}{20} = \frac{4}{5}$

14) $\frac{68}{16} = 4\frac{1}{4}$

15) $\frac{24}{32} = \frac{3}{4}$

16) $\frac{318}{48} = 6\frac{5}{8}$

17) $\frac{5}{15} = \frac{1}{3}$

18) $\frac{36}{45} = \frac{4}{5}$

19) $\frac{9}{18} = \frac{1}{2}$

20) $\frac{424}{48} = 8\frac{5}{6}$

21) $\frac{144}{40} = 3\frac{3}{5}$

22) $\frac{72}{27} = 2\frac{2}{3}$

23) $\frac{20}{40} = \frac{1}{2}$

24) $\frac{18}{36} = \frac{1}{2}$

25) $\frac{105}{20} = 5\frac{1}{4}$

26) $\frac{9}{27} = \frac{1}{3}$

27) $\frac{16}{48} = \frac{1}{3}$

28) $\frac{12}{15} = \frac{4}{5}$

29) $\frac{162}{72} = 2\frac{1}{4}$

30) $\frac{24}{40} = \frac{3}{5}$

31) $\frac{8}{16} = \frac{1}{2}$

32) $\frac{132}{18} = 7\frac{1}{3}$

T) Simplify the fractions.

1) $\frac{292}{32} = 9\frac{1}{8}$

2) $\frac{230}{25} = 9\frac{1}{5}$

3) $\frac{21}{24} = \frac{7}{8}$

4) $\frac{392}{48} = 8\frac{1}{6}$

5) $\frac{18}{27} = \frac{2}{3}$

6) $\frac{9}{12} = \frac{3}{4}$

7) $\frac{132}{24} = 5\frac{1}{2}$

8) $\frac{295}{40} = 7\frac{3}{8}$

9) $\frac{66}{30} = 2\frac{1}{5}$

10) $\frac{69}{9} = 7\frac{2}{3}$

11) $\frac{100}{16} = 6\frac{1}{4}$

12) $\frac{348}{36} = 9\frac{2}{3}$

13) $\frac{12}{16} = \frac{3}{4}$

14) $\frac{6}{18} = \frac{1}{3}$

15) $\frac{2}{8} = \frac{1}{4}$

16) $\frac{343}{35} = 9\frac{4}{5}$

17) $\frac{630}{72} = 8\frac{3}{4}$

18) $\frac{423}{45} = 9\frac{2}{5}$

19) $\frac{105}{42} = 2\frac{1}{2}$

20) $\frac{66}{9} = 7\frac{1}{3}$

21) $\frac{68}{8} = 8\frac{1}{2}$

22) $\frac{60}{16} = 3\frac{3}{4}$

23) $\frac{14}{56} = \frac{1}{4}$

24) $\frac{12}{18} = \frac{2}{3}$

25) $\frac{3}{18} = \frac{1}{6}$

26) $\frac{138}{15} = 9\frac{1}{5}$

27) $\frac{30}{8} = 3\frac{3}{4}$

28) $\frac{20}{40} = \frac{1}{2}$

29) $\frac{77}{21} = 3\frac{2}{3}$

30) $\frac{63}{18} = 3\frac{1}{2}$

31) $\frac{294}{35} = 8\frac{2}{5}$

32) $\frac{25}{40} = \frac{5}{8}$

U) Simplify the fractions.

1) $\frac{168}{18} = 9\frac{1}{3}$ 2) $\frac{68}{16} = 4\frac{1}{4}$ 3) $\frac{322}{56} = 5\frac{3}{4}$ 4) $\frac{24}{48} = \frac{1}{2}$

5) $\frac{54}{9} = 6$ 6) $\frac{120}{20} = 6$ 7) $\frac{56}{8} = 7$ 8) $\frac{54}{6} = 9$

9) $\frac{504}{56} = 9$ 10) $\frac{140}{20} = 7$ 11) $\frac{72}{12} = 6$ 12) $\frac{120}{30} = 4$

13) $\frac{270}{45} = 6$ 14) $\frac{18}{54} = \frac{1}{3}$ 15) $\frac{5}{15} = \frac{1}{3}$ 16) $\frac{22}{8} = 2\frac{3}{4}$

17) $\frac{144}{72} = 2$ 18) $\frac{112}{35} = 3\frac{1}{5}$ 19) $\frac{36}{48} = \frac{3}{4}$ 20) $\frac{44}{12} = 3\frac{2}{3}$

21) $\frac{168}{28} = 6$ 22) $\frac{168}{42} = 4$ 23) $\frac{135}{27} = 5$ 24) $\frac{352}{48} = 7\frac{1}{3}$

25) $\frac{64}{16} = 4$ 26) $\frac{6}{48} = \frac{1}{8}$ 27) $\frac{186}{30} = 6\frac{1}{5}$ 28) $\frac{162}{72} = 2\frac{1}{4}$

29) $\frac{6}{10} = \frac{3}{5}$ 30) $\frac{48}{24} = 2$ 31) $\frac{32}{16} = 2$ 32) $\frac{24}{12} = 2$

V) Simplify the fractions.

1) $\frac{120}{24} = 5$

2) $\frac{120}{40} = 3$

3) $\frac{18}{45} = \frac{2}{5}$

4) $\frac{72}{18} = 4$

5) $\frac{2}{6} = \frac{1}{3}$

6) $\frac{216}{24} = 9$

7) $\frac{144}{48} = 3$

8) $\frac{8}{12} = \frac{2}{3}$

9) $\frac{6}{8} = \frac{3}{4}$

10) $\frac{60}{15} = 4$

11) $\frac{10}{30} = \frac{1}{3}$

12) $\frac{160}{40} = 4$

13) $\frac{45}{72} = \frac{5}{8}$

14) $\frac{18}{27} = \frac{2}{3}$

15) $\frac{48}{24} = 2$

16) $\frac{24}{64} = \frac{3}{8}$

17) $\frac{238}{35} = 6\frac{4}{5}$

18) $\frac{108}{27} = 4$

19) $\frac{2}{8} = \frac{1}{4}$

20) $\frac{6}{18} = \frac{1}{3}$

21) $\frac{375}{40} = 9\frac{3}{8}$

22) $\frac{175}{35} = 5$

23) $\frac{108}{12} = 9$

24) $\frac{280}{40} = 7$

25) $\frac{12}{24} = \frac{1}{2}$

26) $\frac{8}{16} = \frac{1}{2}$

27) $\frac{27}{9} = 3$

28) $\frac{185}{30} = 6\frac{1}{6}$

29) $\frac{125}{25} = 5$

30) $\frac{10}{12} = \frac{5}{6}$

31) $\frac{15}{20} = \frac{3}{4}$

32) $\frac{24}{32} = \frac{3}{4}$

W) Simplify the fractions.

1) $\frac{12}{18} = \frac{2}{3}$

2) $\frac{264}{32} = 8\,\frac{1}{4}$

3) $\frac{48}{24} = 2$

4) $\frac{4}{12} = \frac{1}{3}$

5) $\frac{240}{30} = 8$

6) $\frac{6}{10} = \frac{3}{5}$

7) $\frac{36}{48} = \frac{3}{4}$

8) $\frac{42}{12} = 3\,\frac{1}{2}$

9) $\frac{72}{24} = 3$

10) $\frac{120}{15} = 8$

11) $\frac{216}{72} = 3$

12) $\frac{18}{27} = \frac{2}{3}$

13) $\frac{75}{12} = 6\,\frac{1}{4}$

14) $\frac{423}{45} = 9\,\frac{2}{5}$

15) $\frac{232}{48} = 4\,\frac{5}{6}$

16) $\frac{8}{24} = \frac{1}{3}$

17) $\frac{20}{10} = 2$

18) $\frac{10}{40} = \frac{1}{4}$

19) $\frac{45}{54} = \frac{5}{6}$

20) $\frac{102}{12} = 8\,\frac{1}{2}$

21) $\frac{7}{28} = \frac{1}{4}$

22) $\frac{12}{6} = 2$

23) $\frac{75}{30} = 2\,\frac{1}{2}$

24) $\frac{192}{20} = 9\,\frac{3}{5}$

25) $\frac{8}{32} = \frac{1}{4}$

26) $\frac{88}{24} = 3\,\frac{2}{3}$

27) $\frac{130}{16} = 8\,\frac{1}{8}$

28) $\frac{301}{35} = 8\,\frac{3}{5}$

29) $\frac{9}{36} = \frac{1}{4}$

30) $\frac{72}{9} = 8$

31) $\frac{36}{16} = 2\,\frac{1}{4}$

32) $\frac{336}{48} = 7$

X) Simplify the fractions.

1) $\frac{198}{36} = 5\frac{1}{2}$ 2) $\frac{49}{56} = \frac{7}{8}$ 3) $\frac{56}{8} = 7$ 4) $\frac{240}{40} = 6$

5) $\frac{12}{18} = \frac{2}{3}$ 6) $\frac{72}{36} = 2$ 7) $\frac{65}{25} = 2\frac{3}{5}$ 8) $\frac{40}{6} = 6\frac{2}{3}$

9) $\frac{245}{35} = 7$ 10) $\frac{144}{72} = 2$ 11) $\frac{100}{16} = 6\frac{1}{4}$ 12) $\frac{324}{54} = 6$

13) $\frac{30}{9} = 3\frac{1}{3}$ 14) $\frac{60}{20} = 3$ 15) $\frac{48}{64} = \frac{3}{4}$ 16) $\frac{396}{54} = 7\frac{1}{3}$

17) $\frac{10}{25} = \frac{2}{5}$ 18) $\frac{7}{21} = \frac{1}{3}$ 19) $\frac{74}{10} = 7\frac{2}{5}$ 20) $\frac{441}{72} = 6\frac{1}{8}$

21) $\frac{252}{36} = 7$ 22) $\frac{14}{6} = 2\frac{1}{3}$ 23) $\frac{7}{42} = \frac{1}{6}$ 24) $\frac{108}{27} = 4$

25) $\frac{144}{30} = 4\frac{4}{5}$ 26) $\frac{272}{48} = 5\frac{2}{3}$ 27) $\frac{9}{36} = \frac{1}{4}$ 28) $\frac{18}{24} = \frac{3}{4}$

29) $\frac{96}{48} = 2$ 30) $\frac{192}{24} = 8$ 31) $\frac{102}{30} = 3\frac{2}{5}$ 32) $\frac{108}{12} = 9$

Y) Simplify the fractions.

1) $\frac{100}{25} = 4$

2) $\frac{48}{12} = 4$

3) $\frac{12}{16} = \frac{3}{4}$

4) $\frac{392}{56} = 7$

5) $\frac{133}{21} = 6\frac{1}{3}$

6) $\frac{40}{10} = 4$

7) $\frac{28}{32} = \frac{7}{8}$

8) $\frac{90}{27} = 3\frac{1}{3}$

9) $\frac{210}{35} = 6$

10) $\frac{20}{24} = \frac{5}{6}$

11) $\frac{48}{8} = 6$

12) $\frac{96}{24} = 4$

13) $\frac{8}{12} = \frac{2}{3}$

14) $\frac{96}{16} = 6$

15) $\frac{135}{27} = 5$

16) $\frac{40}{20} = 2$

17) $\frac{438}{48} = 9\frac{1}{8}$

18) $\frac{16}{24} = \frac{2}{3}$

19) $\frac{248}{48} = 5\frac{1}{6}$

20) $\frac{144}{24} = 6$

21) $\frac{111}{12} = 9\frac{1}{4}$

22) $\frac{3}{24} = \frac{1}{8}$

23) $\frac{152}{24} = 6\frac{1}{3}$

24) $\frac{9}{45} = \frac{1}{5}$

25) $\frac{156}{18} = 8\frac{2}{3}$

26) $\frac{204}{24} = 8\frac{1}{2}$

27) $\frac{174}{18} = 9\frac{2}{3}$

28) $\frac{24}{30} = \frac{4}{5}$

29) $\frac{42}{56} = \frac{3}{4}$

30) $\frac{27}{12} = 2\frac{1}{4}$

31) $\frac{188}{20} = 9\frac{2}{5}$

32) $\frac{252}{42} = 6$

Z) Simplify the fractions.

1) $\frac{126}{27} = 4\frac{2}{3}$

2) $\frac{100}{25} = 4$

3) $\frac{3}{9} = \frac{1}{3}$

4) $\frac{8}{16} = \frac{1}{2}$

5) $\frac{216}{24} = 9$

6) $\frac{96}{12} = 8$

7) $\frac{36}{72} = \frac{1}{2}$

8) $\frac{35}{42} = \frac{5}{6}$

9) $\frac{245}{28} = 8\frac{3}{4}$

10) $\frac{4}{12} = \frac{1}{3}$

11) $\frac{145}{25} = 5\frac{4}{5}$

12) $\frac{81}{27} = 3$

13) $\frac{216}{72} = 3$

14) $\frac{111}{12} = 9\frac{1}{4}$

15) $\frac{78}{15} = 5\frac{1}{5}$

16) $\frac{24}{48} = \frac{1}{2}$

17) $\frac{216}{27} = 8$

18) $\frac{14}{16} = \frac{7}{8}$

19) $\frac{182}{28} = 6\frac{1}{2}$

20) $\frac{108}{12} = 9$

21) $\frac{2}{10} = \frac{1}{5}$

22) $\frac{3}{18} = \frac{1}{6}$

23) $\frac{6}{24} = \frac{1}{4}$

24) $\frac{40}{64} = \frac{5}{8}$

25) $\frac{261}{45} = 5\frac{4}{5}$

26) $\frac{24}{6} = 4$

27) $\frac{156}{16} = 9\frac{3}{4}$

28) $\frac{84}{12} = 7$

29) $\frac{36}{18} = 2$

30) $\frac{128}{32} = 4$

31) $\frac{14}{35} = \frac{2}{5}$

32) $\frac{40}{48} = \frac{5}{6}$

AA) Simplify the fractions.

1) $\frac{192}{32}$ = 6

2) $\frac{88}{12}$ = $7\frac{1}{3}$

3) $\frac{22}{10}$ = $2\frac{1}{5}$

4) $\frac{175}{42}$ = $4\frac{1}{6}$

5) $\frac{135}{27}$ = 5

6) $\frac{144}{24}$ = 6

7) $\frac{210}{35}$ = 6

8) $\frac{168}{24}$ = 7

9) $\frac{532}{56}$ = $9\frac{1}{2}$

10) $\frac{224}{32}$ = 7

11) $\frac{104}{16}$ = $6\frac{1}{2}$

12) $\frac{8}{12}$ = $\frac{2}{3}$

13) $\frac{384}{48}$ = 8

14) $\frac{320}{40}$ = 8

15) $\frac{72}{12}$ = 6

16) $\frac{6}{30}$ = $\frac{1}{5}$

17) $\frac{46}{6}$ = $7\frac{2}{3}$

18) $\frac{10}{20}$ = $\frac{1}{2}$

19) $\frac{256}{32}$ = 8

20) $\frac{48}{16}$ = 3

21) $\frac{245}{35}$ = 7

22) $\frac{130}{15}$ = $8\frac{2}{3}$

23) $\frac{352}{64}$ = $5\frac{1}{2}$

24) $\frac{80}{12}$ = $6\frac{2}{3}$

25) $\frac{512}{64}$ = 8

26) $\frac{12}{30}$ = $\frac{2}{5}$

27) $\frac{55}{15}$ = $3\frac{2}{3}$

28) $\frac{20}{30}$ = $\frac{2}{3}$

29) $\frac{6}{8}$ = $\frac{3}{4}$

30) $\frac{639}{72}$ = $8\frac{7}{8}$

31) $\frac{8}{24}$ = $\frac{1}{3}$

32) $\frac{360}{40}$ = 9

BB) Simplify the fractions.

1) $\frac{90}{30} = 3$

2) $\frac{36}{72} = \frac{1}{2}$

3) $\frac{212}{24} = 8\frac{5}{6}$

4) $\frac{152}{20} = 7\frac{3}{5}$

5) $\frac{279}{36} = 7\frac{3}{4}$

6) $\frac{360}{40} = 9$

7) $\frac{4}{6} = \frac{2}{3}$

8) $\frac{108}{36} = 3$

9) $\frac{3}{9} = \frac{1}{3}$

10) $\frac{250}{40} = 6\frac{1}{4}$

11) $\frac{72}{8} = 9$

12) $\frac{45}{15} = 3$

13) $\frac{360}{48} = 7\frac{1}{2}$

14) $\frac{18}{27} = \frac{2}{3}$

15) $\frac{177}{24} = 7\frac{3}{8}$

16) $\frac{240}{40} = 6$

17) $\frac{2}{8} = \frac{1}{4}$

18) $\frac{432}{48} = 9$

19) $\frac{216}{24} = 9$

20) $\frac{42}{48} = \frac{7}{8}$

21) $\frac{162}{18} = 9$

22) $\frac{100}{20} = 5$

23) $\frac{280}{40} = 7$

24) $\frac{270}{54} = 5$

25) $\frac{136}{16} = 8\frac{1}{2}$

26) $\frac{72}{27} = 2\frac{2}{3}$

27) $\frac{531}{72} = 7\frac{3}{8}$

28) $\frac{148}{16} = 9\frac{1}{4}$

29) $\frac{144}{16} = 9$

30) $\frac{210}{36} = 5\frac{5}{6}$

31) $\frac{52}{12} = 4\frac{1}{3}$

32) $\frac{75}{25} = 3$

CC) Simplify the fractions.

1) $\frac{24}{36} = \frac{2}{3}$

2) $\frac{56}{28} = 2$

3) $\frac{46}{6} = 7\frac{2}{3}$

4) $\frac{258}{48} = 5\frac{3}{8}$

5) $\frac{189}{35} = 5\frac{2}{5}$

6) $\frac{210}{30} = 7$

7) $\frac{133}{35} = 3\frac{4}{5}$

8) $\frac{6}{12} = \frac{1}{2}$

9) $\frac{8}{12} = \frac{2}{3}$

10) $\frac{144}{64} = 2\frac{1}{4}$

11) $\frac{72}{27} = 2\frac{2}{3}$

12) $\frac{44}{12} = 3\frac{2}{3}$

13) $\frac{27}{72} = \frac{3}{8}$

14) $\frac{84}{16} = 5\frac{1}{4}$

15) $\frac{161}{35} = 4\frac{3}{5}$

16) $\frac{440}{48} = 9\frac{1}{6}$

17) $\frac{213}{24} = 8\frac{7}{8}$

18) $\frac{216}{27} = 8$

19) $\frac{6}{24} = \frac{1}{4}$

20) $\frac{198}{27} = 7\frac{1}{3}$

21) $\frac{100}{20} = 5$

22) $\frac{14}{42} = \frac{1}{3}$

23) $\frac{315}{72} = 4\frac{3}{8}$

24) $\frac{63}{12} = 5\frac{1}{4}$

25) $\frac{45}{15} = 3$

26) $\frac{324}{36} = 9$

27) $\frac{10}{30} = \frac{1}{3}$

28) $\frac{153}{27} = 5\frac{2}{3}$

29) $\frac{120}{24} = 5$

30) $\frac{3}{12} = \frac{1}{4}$

31) $\frac{147}{15} = 9\frac{4}{5}$

32) $\frac{60}{15} = 4$

DD) Simplify the fractions.

1) $\frac{57}{8} = 7\frac{1}{8}$

2) $\frac{160}{32} = 5$

3) $\frac{32}{40} = \frac{4}{5}$

4) $\frac{92}{24} = 3\frac{5}{6}$

5) $\frac{12}{16} = \frac{3}{4}$

6) $\frac{49}{56} = \frac{7}{8}$

7) $\frac{48}{24} = 2$

8) $\frac{4}{8} = \frac{1}{2}$

9) $\frac{114}{18} = 6\frac{1}{3}$

10) $\frac{9}{15} = \frac{3}{5}$

11) $\frac{36}{48} = \frac{3}{4}$

12) $\frac{132}{30} = 4\frac{2}{5}$

13) $\frac{36}{54} = \frac{2}{3}$

14) $\frac{98}{16} = 6\frac{1}{8}$

15) $\frac{33}{9} = 3\frac{2}{3}$

16) $\frac{32}{8} = 4$

17) $\frac{230}{30} = 7\frac{2}{3}$

18) $\frac{80}{25} = 3\frac{1}{5}$

19) $\frac{280}{40} = 7$

20) $\frac{15}{20} = \frac{3}{4}$

21) $\frac{156}{18} = 8\frac{2}{3}$

22) $\frac{24}{64} = \frac{3}{8}$

23) $\frac{32}{48} = \frac{2}{3}$

24) $\frac{108}{12} = 9$

25) $\frac{110}{20} = 5\frac{1}{2}$

26) $\frac{245}{35} = 7$

27) $\frac{60}{20} = 3$

28) $\frac{140}{24} = 5\frac{5}{6}$

29) $\frac{3}{12} = \frac{1}{4}$

30) $\frac{224}{32} = 7$

31) $\frac{98}{21} = 4\frac{2}{3}$

32) $\frac{162}{27} = 6$

EE) Simplify the fractions.

1) $\frac{360}{60} = 6$

2) $\frac{14}{42} = \frac{1}{3}$

3) $\frac{504}{126} = 4$

4) $\frac{60}{8} = 7\,\frac{1}{2}$

5) $\frac{420}{60} = 7$

6) $\frac{94}{16} = 5\,\frac{7}{8}$

7) $\frac{792}{128} = 6\,\frac{3}{16}$

8) $\frac{7}{14} = \frac{1}{2}$

9) $\frac{6}{18} = \frac{1}{3}$

10) $\frac{21}{27} = \frac{7}{9}$

11) $\frac{204}{68} = 3$

12) $\frac{180}{56} = 3\,\frac{3}{14}$

13) $\frac{265}{50} = 5\,\frac{3}{10}$

14) $\frac{186}{36} = 5\,\frac{1}{6}$

15) $\frac{2}{36} = \frac{1}{18}$

16) $\frac{120}{20} = 6$

17) $\frac{108}{45} = 2\,\frac{2}{5}$

18) $\frac{222}{42} = 5\,\frac{2}{7}$

19) $\frac{480}{88} = 5\,\frac{5}{11}$

20) $\frac{96}{48} = 2$

21) $\frac{258}{26} = 9\,\frac{12}{13}$

22) $\frac{270}{90} = 3$

23) $\frac{366}{57} = 6\,\frac{8}{19}$

24) $\frac{300}{100} = 3$

25) $\frac{282}{36} = 7\,\frac{5}{6}$

26) $\frac{603}{171} = 3\,\frac{10}{19}$

27) $\frac{24}{36} = \frac{2}{3}$

28) $\frac{94}{24} = 3\,\frac{11}{12}$

29) $\frac{609}{63} = 9\,\frac{2}{3}$

30) $\frac{9}{117} = \frac{1}{13}$

31) $\frac{268}{28} = 9\,\frac{4}{7}$

32) $\frac{56}{126} = \frac{4}{9}$

FF) Simplify the fractions.

1) $\frac{64}{24} = 2\frac{2}{3}$

2) $\frac{492}{54} = 9\frac{1}{9}$

3) $\frac{28}{84} = \frac{1}{3}$

4) $\frac{655}{90} = 7\frac{5}{18}$

5) $\frac{36}{48} = \frac{3}{4}$

6) $\frac{1665}{180} = 9\frac{1}{4}$

7) $\frac{392}{56} = 7$

8) $\frac{450}{135} = 3\frac{1}{3}$

9) $\frac{150}{25} = 6$

10) $\frac{288}{32} = 9$

11) $\frac{16}{68} = \frac{4}{17}$

12) $\frac{176}{22} = 8$

13) $\frac{6}{12} = \frac{1}{2}$

14) $\frac{513}{90} = 5\frac{7}{10}$

15) $\frac{18}{36} = \frac{1}{2}$

16) $\frac{27}{99} = \frac{3}{11}$

17) $\frac{198}{21} = 9\frac{3}{7}$

18) $\frac{630}{105} = 6$

19) $\frac{57}{27} = 2\frac{1}{9}$

20) $\frac{288}{48} = 6$

21) $\frac{84}{133} = \frac{12}{19}$

22) $\frac{360}{72} = 5$

23) $\frac{4}{6} = \frac{2}{3}$

24) $\frac{610}{65} = 9\frac{5}{13}$

25) $\frac{406}{42} = 9\frac{2}{3}$

26) $\frac{413}{98} = 4\frac{3}{14}$

27) $\frac{275}{90} = 3\frac{1}{18}$

28) $\frac{80}{40} = 2$

29) $\frac{264}{40} = 6\frac{3}{5}$

30) $\frac{148}{34} = 4\frac{6}{17}$

31) $\frac{54}{72} = \frac{3}{4}$

32) $\frac{360}{45} = 8$

GG) Simplify the fractions.

1) $\frac{3}{9} = \frac{1}{3}$

2) $\frac{18}{84} = \frac{3}{14}$

3) $\frac{134}{40} = 3\,\frac{7}{20}$

4) $\frac{84}{15} = 5\,\frac{3}{5}$

5) $\frac{800}{90} = 8\,\frac{8}{9}$

6) $\frac{243}{27} = 9$

7) $\frac{32}{8} = 4$

8) $\frac{400}{104} = 3\,\frac{11}{13}$

9) $\frac{42}{119} = \frac{6}{17}$

10) $\frac{4}{16} = \frac{1}{4}$

11) $\frac{6}{24} = \frac{1}{4}$

12) $\frac{360}{63} = 5\,\frac{5}{7}$

13) $\frac{198}{54} = 3\,\frac{2}{3}$

14) $\frac{88}{96} = \frac{11}{12}$

15) $\frac{150}{50} = 3$

16) $\frac{36}{44} = \frac{9}{11}$

17) $\frac{5}{80} = \frac{1}{16}$

18) $\frac{420}{60} = 7$

19) $\frac{312}{48} = 6\,\frac{1}{2}$

20) $\frac{88}{32} = 2\,\frac{3}{4}$

21) $\frac{189}{21} = 9$

22) $\frac{675}{135} = 5$

23) $\frac{1053}{117} = 9$

24) $\frac{632}{128} = 4\,\frac{15}{16}$

25) $\frac{3}{6} = \frac{1}{2}$

26) $\frac{474}{72} = 6\,\frac{7}{12}$

27) $\frac{612}{114} = 5\,\frac{7}{19}$

28) $\frac{340}{55} = 6\,\frac{2}{11}$

29) $\frac{632}{72} = 8\,\frac{7}{9}$

30) $\frac{42}{108} = \frac{7}{18}$

31) $\frac{96}{120} = \frac{4}{5}$

32) $\frac{88}{34} = 2\,\frac{10}{17}$

HH) Simplify the fractions.

1) $\frac{32}{16} = 2$

2) $\frac{9}{12} = \frac{3}{4}$

3) $\frac{6}{12} = \frac{1}{2}$

4) $\frac{945}{133} = 7\frac{2}{19}$

5) $\frac{90}{117} = \frac{10}{13}$

6) $\frac{111}{27} = 4\frac{1}{9}$

7) $\frac{220}{38} = 5\frac{15}{19}$

8) $\frac{30}{32} = \frac{15}{16}$

9) $\frac{16}{44} = \frac{4}{11}$

10) $\frac{259}{42} = 6\frac{1}{6}$

11) $\frac{38}{4} = 9\frac{1}{2}$

12) $\frac{270}{45} = 6$

13) $\frac{600}{84} = 7\frac{1}{7}$

14) $\frac{66}{30} = 2\frac{1}{5}$

15) $\frac{105}{21} = 5$

16) $\frac{972}{108} = 9$

17) $\frac{90}{108} = \frac{5}{6}$

18) $\frac{520}{104} = 5$

19) $\frac{248}{80} = 3\frac{1}{10}$

20) $\frac{14}{34} = \frac{7}{17}$

21) $\frac{45}{75} = \frac{3}{5}$

22) $\frac{108}{27} = 4$

23) $\frac{360}{40} = 9$

24) $\frac{180}{24} = 7\frac{1}{2}$

25) $\frac{476}{119} = 4$

26) $\frac{351}{117} = 3$

27) $\frac{333}{72} = 4\frac{5}{8}$

28) $\frac{24}{40} = \frac{3}{5}$

29) $\frac{352}{80} = 4\frac{2}{5}$

30) $\frac{270}{90} = 3$

31) $\frac{18}{27} = \frac{2}{3}$

32) $\frac{513}{171} = 3$

II) Simplify the fractions.

1) $\frac{80}{88} = \frac{10}{11}$

2) $\frac{18}{114} = \frac{3}{19}$

3) $\frac{216}{24} = 9$

4) $\frac{360}{45} = 8$

5) $\frac{25}{30} = \frac{5}{6}$

6) $\frac{459}{144} = 3\,\frac{3}{16}$

7) $\frac{6}{30} = \frac{1}{5}$

8) $\frac{14}{63} = \frac{2}{9}$

9) $\frac{588}{84} = 7$

10) $\frac{7}{91} = \frac{1}{13}$

11) $\frac{568}{104} = 5\,\frac{6}{13}$

12) $\frac{16}{48} = \frac{1}{3}$

13) $\frac{312}{40} = 7\,\frac{4}{5}$

14) $\frac{52}{72} = \frac{13}{18}$

15) $\frac{222}{102} = 2\,\frac{3}{17}$

16) $\frac{585}{60} = 9\,\frac{3}{4}$

17) $\frac{291}{42} = 6\,\frac{13}{14}$

18) $\frac{3}{6} = \frac{1}{2}$

19) $\frac{3}{60} = \frac{1}{20}$

20) $\frac{567}{81} = 7$

21) $\frac{336}{40} = 8\,\frac{2}{5}$

22) $\frac{60}{20} = 3$

23) $\frac{45}{55} = \frac{9}{11}$

24) $\frac{1064}{152} = 7$

25) $\frac{45}{75} = \frac{3}{5}$

26) $\frac{4}{16} = \frac{1}{4}$

27) $\frac{196}{21} = 9\,\frac{1}{3}$

28) $\frac{98}{49} = 2$

29) $\frac{1112}{128} = 8\,\frac{11}{16}$

30) $\frac{348}{102} = 3\,\frac{7}{17}$

31) $\frac{240}{48} = 5$

32) $\frac{16}{28} = \frac{4}{7}$

JJ) Simplify the fractions.

1) $\frac{25}{10} = 2\frac{1}{2}$

2) $\frac{225}{45} = 5$

3) $\frac{238}{119} = 2$

4) $\frac{80}{96} = \frac{5}{6}$

5) $\frac{48}{24} = 2$

6) $\frac{10}{30} = \frac{1}{3}$

7) $\frac{78}{120} = \frac{13}{20}$

8) $\frac{378}{49} = 7\frac{5}{7}$

9) $\frac{525}{75} = 7$

10) $\frac{312}{40} = 7\frac{4}{5}$

11) $\frac{125}{15} = 8\frac{1}{3}$

12) $\frac{540}{65} = 8\frac{4}{13}$

13) $\frac{152}{38} = 4$

14) $\frac{432}{72} = 6$

15) $\frac{108}{54} = 2$

16) $\frac{76}{32} = 2\frac{3}{8}$

17) $\frac{6}{12} = \frac{1}{2}$

18) $\frac{27}{144} = \frac{3}{16}$

19) $\frac{549}{72} = 7\frac{5}{8}$

20) $\frac{336}{42} = 8$

21) $\frac{42}{10} = 4\frac{1}{5}$

22) $\frac{665}{77} = 8\frac{7}{11}$

23) $\frac{285}{60} = 4\frac{3}{4}$

24) $\frac{55}{95} = \frac{11}{19}$

25) $\frac{96}{48} = 2$

26) $\frac{294}{42} = 7$

27) $\frac{112}{119} = \frac{16}{17}$

28) $\frac{630}{126} = 5$

29) $\frac{7}{28} = \frac{1}{4}$

30) $\frac{3}{9} = \frac{1}{3}$

31) $\frac{20}{45} = \frac{4}{9}$

32) $\frac{702}{117} = 6$

KK) Simplify the fractions.

1) $\frac{60}{96} = \frac{5}{8}$

2) $\frac{272}{104} = 2\frac{8}{13}$

3) $\frac{180}{60} = 3$

4) $\frac{95}{25} = 3\frac{4}{5}$

5) $\frac{990}{171} = 5\frac{15}{19}$

6) $\frac{840}{120} = 7$

7) $\frac{360}{54} = 6\frac{2}{3}$

8) $\frac{6}{33} = \frac{2}{11}$

9) $\frac{42}{102} = \frac{7}{17}$

10) $\frac{168}{56} = 3$

11) $\frac{196}{98} = 2$

12) $\frac{480}{60} = 8$

13) $\frac{9}{45} = \frac{1}{5}$

14) $\frac{84}{16} = 5\frac{1}{4}$

15) $\frac{624}{78} = 8$

16) $\frac{378}{126} = 3$

17) $\frac{12}{84} = \frac{1}{7}$

18) $\frac{702}{90} = 7\frac{4}{5}$

19) $\frac{90}{18} = 5$

20) $\frac{54}{18} = 3$

21) $\frac{336}{36} = 9\frac{1}{3}$

22) $\frac{144}{18} = 8$

23) $\frac{576}{64} = 9$

24) $\frac{497}{112} = 4\frac{7}{16}$

25) $\frac{624}{96} = 6\frac{1}{2}$

26) $\frac{39}{57} = \frac{13}{19}$

27) $\frac{750}{120} = 6\frac{1}{4}$

28) $\frac{528}{88} = 6$

29) $\frac{690}{85} = 8\frac{2}{17}$

30) $\frac{732}{90} = 8\frac{2}{15}$

31) $\frac{882}{180} = 4\frac{9}{10}$

32) $\frac{171}{27} = 6\frac{1}{3}$

LL) Simplify the fractions.

1) $\frac{450}{90} = 5$

2) $\frac{560}{80} = 7$

3) $\frac{297}{99} = 3$

4) $\frac{5}{25} = \frac{1}{5}$

5) $\frac{1440}{160} = 9$

6) $\frac{1296}{144} = 9$

7) $\frac{408}{48} = 8\frac{1}{2}$

8) $\frac{30}{34} = \frac{15}{17}$

9) $\frac{48}{24} = 2$

10) $\frac{510}{70} = 7\frac{2}{7}$

11) $\frac{264}{48} = 5\frac{1}{2}$

12) $\frac{6}{24} = \frac{1}{4}$

13) $\frac{144}{24} = 6$

14) $\frac{26}{38} = \frac{13}{19}$

15) $\frac{477}{117} = 4\frac{1}{13}$

16) $\frac{28}{36} = \frac{7}{9}$

17) $\frac{735}{105} = 7$

18) $\frac{576}{72} = 8$

19) $\frac{539}{77} = 7$

20) $\frac{48}{136} = \frac{6}{17}$

21) $\frac{78}{8} = 9\frac{3}{4}$

22) $\frac{54}{18} = 3$

23) $\frac{10}{30} = \frac{1}{3}$

24) $\frac{980}{140} = 7$

25) $\frac{96}{48} = 2$

26) $\frac{76}{36} = 2\frac{1}{9}$

27) $\frac{205}{35} = 5\frac{6}{7}$

28) $\frac{210}{30} = 7$

29) $\frac{567}{112} = 5\frac{1}{16}$

30) $\frac{126}{14} = 9$

31) $\frac{8}{40} = \frac{1}{5}$

32) $\frac{81}{108} = \frac{3}{4}$

MM) Simplify the fractions.

1) $\frac{56}{126} = \frac{4}{9}$

2) $\frac{18}{72} = \frac{1}{4}$

3) $\frac{416}{44} = 9\,\frac{5}{11}$

4) $\frac{686}{98} = 7$

5) $\frac{252}{42} = 6$

6) $\frac{90}{25} = 3\,\frac{3}{5}$

7) $\frac{171}{51} = 3\,\frac{6}{17}$

8) $\frac{36}{60} = \frac{3}{5}$

9) $\frac{88}{44} = 2$

10) $\frac{6}{24} = \frac{1}{4}$

11) $\frac{8}{16} = \frac{1}{2}$

12) $\frac{124}{32} = 3\,\frac{7}{8}$

13) $\frac{35}{98} = \frac{5}{14}$

14) $\frac{800}{100} = 8$

15) $\frac{342}{108} = 3\,\frac{1}{6}$

16) $\frac{28}{36} = \frac{7}{9}$

17) $\frac{285}{57} = 5$

18) $\frac{36}{72} = \frac{1}{2}$

19) $\frac{60}{30} = 2$

20) $\frac{24}{60} = \frac{2}{5}$

21) $\frac{14}{16} = \frac{7}{8}$

22) $\frac{226}{26} = 8\,\frac{9}{13}$

23) $\frac{48}{9} = 5\,\frac{1}{3}$

24) $\frac{84}{108} = \frac{7}{9}$

25) $\frac{1071}{153} = 7$

26) $\frac{64}{152} = \frac{8}{19}$

27) $\frac{228}{60} = 3\,\frac{4}{5}$

28) $\frac{22}{4} = 5\,\frac{1}{2}$

29) $\frac{328}{80} = 4\,\frac{1}{10}$

30) $\frac{5}{15} = \frac{1}{3}$

31) $\frac{522}{66} = 7\,\frac{10}{11}$

32) $\frac{168}{24} = 7$

NN) Simplify the fractions.

1) $\frac{220}{44} = 5$

2) $\frac{720}{144} = 5$

3) $\frac{6}{60} = \frac{1}{10}$

4) $\frac{1728}{180} = 9\frac{3}{5}$

5) $\frac{54}{84} = \frac{9}{14}$

6) $\frac{20}{24} = \frac{5}{6}$

7) $\frac{175}{35} = 5$

8) $\frac{675}{75} = 9$

9) $\frac{665}{95} = 7$

10) $\frac{104}{12} = 8\frac{2}{3}$

11) $\frac{135}{15} = 9$

12) $\frac{160}{48} = 3\frac{1}{3}$

13) $\frac{28}{36} = \frac{7}{9}$

14) $\frac{86}{34} = 2\frac{9}{17}$

15) $\frac{54}{63} = \frac{6}{7}$

16) $\frac{12}{60} = \frac{1}{5}$

17) $\frac{170}{65} = 2\frac{8}{13}$

18) $\frac{36}{108} = \frac{1}{3}$

19) $\frac{21}{45} = \frac{7}{15}$

20) $\frac{90}{15} = 6$

21) $\frac{476}{77} = 6\frac{2}{11}$

22) $\frac{63}{72} = \frac{7}{8}$

23) $\frac{115}{20} = 5\frac{3}{4}$

24) $\frac{14}{24} = \frac{7}{12}$

25) $\frac{624}{84} = 7\frac{3}{7}$

26) $\frac{5}{10} = \frac{1}{2}$

27) $\frac{820}{95} = 8\frac{12}{19}$

28) $\frac{700}{140} = 5$

29) $\frac{40}{64} = \frac{5}{8}$

30) $\frac{104}{52} = 2$

31) $\frac{210}{30} = 7$

32) $\frac{864}{144} = 6$

OO) Simplify the fractions.

1) $\frac{927}{270} = 3\frac{13}{30}$

2) $\frac{20}{110} = \frac{2}{11}$

3) $\frac{138}{150} = \frac{23}{25}$

4) $\frac{15}{75} = \frac{1}{5}$

5) $\frac{469}{84} = 5\frac{7}{12}$

6) $\frac{95}{15} = 6\frac{1}{3}$

7) $\frac{128}{28} = 4\frac{4}{7}$

8) $\frac{63}{162} = \frac{7}{18}$

9) $\frac{4050}{450} = 9$

10) $\frac{4}{28} = \frac{1}{7}$

11) $\frac{32}{4} = 8$

12) $\frac{1182}{120} = 9\frac{17}{20}$

13) $\frac{234}{39} = 6$

14) $\frac{1408}{400} = 3\frac{13}{25}$

15) $\frac{230}{45} = 5\frac{1}{9}$

16) $\frac{6}{32} = \frac{3}{16}$

17) $\frac{1728}{240} = 7\frac{1}{5}$

18) $\frac{640}{80} = 8$

19) $\frac{360}{120} = 3$

20) $\frac{65}{105} = \frac{13}{21}$

21) $\frac{5600}{700} = 8$

22) $\frac{398}{40} = 9\frac{19}{20}$

23) $\frac{8}{32} = \frac{1}{4}$

24) $\frac{248}{44} = 5\frac{7}{11}$

25) $\frac{20}{32} = \frac{5}{8}$

26) $\frac{54}{207} = \frac{6}{23}$

27) $\frac{760}{152} = 5$

28) $\frac{18}{153} = \frac{2}{17}$

29) $\frac{232}{40} = 5\frac{4}{5}$

30) $\frac{4}{12} = \frac{1}{3}$

31) $\frac{1200}{240} = 5$

32) $\frac{375}{75} = 5$

PP) Simplify the fractions.

1) $\frac{54}{10} = 5\frac{2}{5}$

2) $\frac{214}{38} = 5\frac{12}{19}$

3) $\frac{72}{126} = \frac{4}{7}$

4) $\frac{483}{161} = 3$

5) $\frac{816}{200} = 4\frac{2}{25}$

6) $\frac{438}{96} = 4\frac{9}{16}$

7) $\frac{153}{36} = 4\frac{1}{4}$

8) $\frac{26}{60} = \frac{13}{30}$

9) $\frac{3696}{700} = 5\frac{7}{25}$

10) $\frac{336}{48} = 7$

11) $\frac{80}{40} = 2$

12) $\frac{6}{42} = \frac{1}{7}$

13) $\frac{360}{85} = 4\frac{4}{17}$

14) $\frac{130}{26} = 5$

15) $\frac{148}{44} = 3\frac{4}{11}$

16) $\frac{791}{140} = 5\frac{13}{20}$

17) $\frac{324}{108} = 3$

18) $\frac{952}{96} = 9\frac{11}{12}$

19) $\frac{228}{240} = \frac{19}{20}$

20) $\frac{388}{88} = 4\frac{9}{22}$

21) $\frac{273}{91} = 3$

22) $\frac{25}{35} = \frac{5}{7}$

23) $\frac{60}{72} = \frac{5}{6}$

24) $\frac{539}{210} = 2\frac{17}{30}$

25) $\frac{28}{32} = \frac{7}{8}$

26) $\frac{597}{120} = 4\frac{39}{40}$

27) $\frac{96}{16} = 6$

28) $\frac{484}{96} = 5\frac{1}{24}$

29) $\frac{12}{20} = \frac{3}{5}$

30) $\frac{1000}{112} = 8\frac{13}{14}$

31) $\frac{55}{75} = \frac{11}{15}$

32) $\frac{170}{18} = 9\frac{4}{9}$

QQ) Simplify the fractions.

1) $\frac{378}{189} = 2$

2) $\frac{84}{140} = \frac{3}{5}$

3) $\frac{3150}{450} = 7$

4) $\frac{50}{10} = 5$

5) $\frac{16}{96} = \frac{1}{6}$

6) $\frac{56}{12} = 4\frac{2}{3}$

7) $\frac{342}{135} = 2\frac{8}{15}$

8) $\frac{245}{35} = 7$

9) $\frac{1350}{225} = 6$

10) $\frac{231}{77} = 3$

11) $\frac{3}{39} = \frac{1}{13}$

12) $\frac{85}{120} = \frac{17}{24}$

13) $\frac{171}{57} = 3$

14) $\frac{364}{56} = 6\frac{1}{2}$

15) $\frac{256}{480} = \frac{8}{15}$

16) $\frac{183}{30} = 6\frac{1}{10}$

17) $\frac{2380}{420} = 5\frac{2}{3}$

18) $\frac{144}{16} = 9$

19) $\frac{268}{44} = 6\frac{1}{11}$

20) $\frac{18}{24} = \frac{3}{4}$

21) $\frac{189}{21} = 9$

22) $\frac{196}{28} = 7$

23) $\frac{544}{80} = 6\frac{4}{5}$

24) $\frac{1440}{160} = 9$

25) $\frac{546}{108} = 5\frac{1}{18}$

26) $\frac{609}{63} = 9\frac{2}{3}$

27) $\frac{24}{60} = \frac{2}{5}$

28) $\frac{84}{225} = \frac{28}{75}$

29) $\frac{1272}{400} = 3\frac{9}{50}$

30) $\frac{546}{91} = 6$

31) $\frac{450}{207} = 2\frac{4}{23}$

32) $\frac{66}{12} = 5\frac{1}{2}$

RR) Simplify the fractions.

1) $\frac{8}{136} = \frac{1}{17}$

2) $\frac{738}{138} = 5\frac{8}{23}$

3) $\frac{240}{120} = 2$

4) $\frac{168}{32} = 5\frac{1}{4}$

5) $\frac{48}{15} = 3\frac{1}{5}$

6) $\frac{168}{24} = 7$

7) $\frac{20}{28} = \frac{5}{7}$

8) $\frac{696}{150} = 4\frac{16}{25}$

9) $\frac{1920}{320} = 6$

10) $\frac{969}{150} = 6\frac{23}{50}$

11) $\frac{48}{16} = 3$

12) $\frac{42}{77} = \frac{6}{11}$

13) $\frac{1050}{150} = 7$

14) $\frac{1368}{152} = 9$

15) $\frac{117}{180} = \frac{13}{20}$

16) $\frac{378}{63} = 6$

17) $\frac{48}{24} = 2$

18) $\frac{504}{56} = 9$

19) $\frac{154}{22} = 7$

20) $\frac{18}{90} = \frac{1}{5}$

21) $\frac{44}{64} = \frac{11}{16}$

22) $\frac{1449}{153} = 9\frac{8}{17}$

23) $\frac{240}{80} = 3$

24) $\frac{1288}{161} = 8$

25) $\frac{632}{192} = 3\frac{7}{24}$

26) $\frac{450}{50} = 9$

27) $\frac{112}{133} = \frac{16}{19}$

28) $\frac{8}{12} = \frac{2}{3}$

29) $\frac{4}{18} = \frac{2}{9}$

30) $\frac{68}{100} = \frac{17}{25}$

31) $\frac{10}{26} = \frac{5}{13}$

32) $\frac{4986}{540} = 9\frac{7}{30}$

SS) Simplify the fractions.

1) $\frac{745}{85} = 8\frac{13}{17}$

2) $\frac{1505}{525} = 2\frac{13}{15}$

3) $\frac{560}{96} = 5\frac{5}{6}$

4) $\frac{152}{76} = 2$

5) $\frac{700}{100} = 7$

6) $\frac{114}{54} = 2\frac{1}{9}$

7) $\frac{32}{50} = \frac{16}{25}$

8) $\frac{196}{49} = 4$

9) $\frac{12}{30} = \frac{2}{5}$

10) $\frac{198}{48} = 4\frac{1}{8}$

11) $\frac{2781}{360} = 7\frac{29}{40}$

12) $\frac{1096}{112} = 9\frac{11}{14}$

13) $\frac{441}{48} = 9\frac{3}{16}$

14) $\frac{180}{30} = 6$

15) $\frac{440}{104} = 4\frac{3}{13}$

16) $\frac{528}{66} = 8$

17) $\frac{162}{54} = 3$

18) $\frac{432}{48} = 9$

19) $\frac{405}{125} = 3\frac{6}{25}$

20) $\frac{1125}{225} = 5$

21) $\frac{42}{138} = \frac{7}{23}$

22) $\frac{54}{120} = \frac{9}{20}$

23) $\frac{18}{126} = \frac{1}{7}$

24) $\frac{900}{300} = 3$

25) $\frac{15}{36} = \frac{5}{12}$

26) $\frac{1656}{300} = 5\frac{13}{25}$

27) $\frac{1080}{120} = 9$

28) $\frac{8}{28} = \frac{2}{7}$

29) $\frac{1605}{180} = 8\frac{11}{12}$

30) $\frac{56}{126} = \frac{4}{9}$

31) $\frac{112}{14} = 8$

32) $\frac{12}{18} = \frac{2}{3}$

TT) Simplify the fractions.

1) $\frac{18}{81} = \frac{2}{9}$

2) $\frac{175}{35} = 5$

3) $\frac{256}{32} = 8$

4) $\frac{10}{70} = \frac{1}{7}$

5) $\frac{140}{420} = \frac{1}{3}$

6) $\frac{54}{63} = \frac{6}{7}$

7) $\frac{18}{9} = 2$

8) $\frac{810}{90} = 9$

9) $\frac{40}{75} = \frac{8}{15}$

10) $\frac{644}{91} = 7\,\frac{1}{13}$

11) $\frac{300}{75} = 4$

12) $\frac{87}{90} = \frac{29}{30}$

13) $\frac{12}{68} = \frac{3}{17}$

14) $\frac{40}{10} = 4$

15) $\frac{12}{69} = \frac{4}{23}$

16) $\frac{1360}{480} = 2\,\frac{5}{6}$

17) $\frac{7}{28} = \frac{1}{4}$

18) $\frac{182}{20} = 9\,\frac{1}{10}$

19) $\frac{150}{30} = 5$

20) $\frac{30}{10} = 3$

21) $\frac{450}{70} = 6\,\frac{3}{7}$

22) $\frac{1400}{154} = 9\,\frac{1}{11}$

23) $\frac{9}{27} = \frac{1}{3}$

24) $\frac{882}{126} = 7$

25) $\frac{90}{117} = \frac{10}{13}$

26) $\frac{324}{81} = 4$

27) $\frac{840}{168} = 5$

28) $\frac{195}{33} = 5\,\frac{10}{11}$

29) $\frac{894}{90} = 9\,\frac{14}{15}$

30) $\frac{252}{675} = \frac{28}{75}$

31) $\frac{1016}{152} = 6\,\frac{13}{19}$

32) $\frac{1440}{240} = 6$

UU) Simplify the fractions.

1) $\frac{900}{180} = 5$

2) $\frac{222}{60} = 3\frac{7}{10}$

3) $\frac{567}{189} = 3$

4) $\frac{24}{32} = \frac{3}{4}$

5) $\frac{320}{100} = 3\frac{1}{5}$

6) $\frac{225}{45} = 5$

7) $\frac{1152}{128} = 9$

8) $\frac{270}{30} = 9$

9) $\frac{480}{96} = 5$

10) $\frac{50}{150} = \frac{1}{3}$

11) $\frac{30}{55} = \frac{6}{11}$

12) $\frac{420}{105} = 4$

13) $\frac{264}{44} = 6$

14) $\frac{92}{100} = \frac{23}{25}$

15) $\frac{84}{42} = 2$

16) $\frac{32}{48} = \frac{2}{3}$

17) $\frac{40}{80} = \frac{1}{2}$

18) $\frac{2}{4} = \frac{1}{2}$

19) $\frac{453}{48} = 9\frac{7}{16}$

20) $\frac{441}{81} = 5\frac{4}{9}$

21) $\frac{8}{32} = \frac{1}{4}$

22) $\frac{150}{16} = 9\frac{3}{8}$

23) $\frac{2400}{300} = 8$

24) $\frac{16}{20} = \frac{4}{5}$

25) $\frac{162}{57} = 2\frac{16}{19}$

26) $\frac{2070}{360} = 5\frac{3}{4}$

27) $\frac{816}{102} = 8$

28) $\frac{88}{100} = \frac{22}{25}$

29) $\frac{480}{80} = 6$

30) $\frac{18}{27} = \frac{2}{3}$

31) $\frac{270}{108} = 2\frac{1}{2}$

32) $\frac{4270}{500} = 8\frac{27}{50}$

VV) Simplify the fractions.

1) $\frac{1440}{360} = 4$

2) $\frac{1680}{240} = 7$

3) $\frac{45}{81} = \frac{5}{9}$

4) $\frac{960}{132} = 7\frac{3}{11}$

5) $\frac{384}{96} = 4$

6) $\frac{7}{42} = \frac{1}{6}$

7) $\frac{33}{36} = \frac{11}{12}$

8) $\frac{72}{144} = \frac{1}{2}$

9) $\frac{120}{150} = \frac{4}{5}$

10) $\frac{1170}{360} = 3\frac{1}{4}$

11) $\frac{6}{21} = \frac{2}{7}$

12) $\frac{20}{64} = \frac{5}{16}$

13) $\frac{708}{114} = 6\frac{4}{19}$

14) $\frac{133}{14} = 9\frac{1}{2}$

15) $\frac{144}{40} = 3\frac{3}{5}$

16) $\frac{320}{85} = 3\frac{13}{17}$

17) $\frac{414}{69} = 6$

18) $\frac{528}{90} = 5\frac{13}{15}$

19) $\frac{940}{100} = 9\frac{2}{5}$

20) $\frac{576}{72} = 8$

21) $\frac{532}{80} = 6\frac{13}{20}$

22) $\frac{847}{98} = 8\frac{9}{14}$

23) $\frac{345}{500} = \frac{69}{100}$

24) $\frac{147}{63} = 2\frac{1}{3}$

25) $\frac{4}{48} = \frac{1}{12}$

26) $\frac{30}{6} = 5$

27) $\frac{1152}{144} = 8$

28) $\frac{104}{26} = 4$

29) $\frac{738}{99} = 7\frac{5}{11}$

30) $\frac{70}{98} = \frac{5}{7}$

31) $\frac{8}{16} = \frac{1}{2}$

32) $\frac{8}{28} = \frac{2}{7}$

WW) Simplify the fractions.

1) $\frac{288}{36} = 8$

2) $\frac{6}{34} = \frac{3}{17}$

3) $\frac{18}{48} = \frac{3}{8}$

4) $\frac{98}{105} = \frac{14}{15}$

5) $\frac{150}{375} = \frac{2}{5}$

6) $\frac{666}{72} = 9\frac{1}{4}$

7) $\frac{308}{49} = 6\frac{2}{7}$

8) $\frac{16}{480} = \frac{1}{30}$

9) $\frac{40}{44} = \frac{10}{11}$

10) $\frac{102}{15} = 6\frac{4}{5}$

11) $\frac{38}{60} = \frac{19}{30}$

12) $\frac{400}{80} = 5$

13) $\frac{5}{115} = \frac{1}{23}$

14) $\frac{1071}{198} = 5\frac{9}{22}$

15) $\frac{9}{189} = \frac{1}{21}$

16) $\frac{152}{38} = 4$

17) $\frac{228}{54} = 4\frac{2}{9}$

18) $\frac{450}{150} = 3$

19) $\frac{91}{168} = \frac{13}{24}$

20) $\frac{54}{27} = 2$

21) $\frac{96}{112} = \frac{6}{7}$

22) $\frac{840}{240} = 3\frac{1}{2}$

23) $\frac{12}{51} = \frac{4}{17}$

24) $\frac{84}{360} = \frac{7}{30}$

25) $\frac{220}{55} = 4$

26) $\frac{266}{28} = 9\frac{1}{2}$

27) $\frac{56}{28} = 2$

28) $\frac{144}{150} = \frac{24}{25}$

29) $\frac{666}{84} = 7\frac{13}{14}$

30) $\frac{567}{63} = 9$

31) $\frac{63}{112} = \frac{9}{16}$

32) $\frac{14}{38} = \frac{7}{19}$

XX) Simplify the fractions.

1) $\frac{561}{66} = 8\frac{1}{2}$

2) $\frac{296}{88} = 3\frac{4}{11}$

3) $\frac{175}{60} = 2\frac{11}{12}$

4) $\frac{342}{450} = \frac{19}{25}$

5) $\frac{84}{126} = \frac{2}{3}$

6) $\frac{357}{51} = 7$

7) $\frac{1056}{150} = 7\frac{1}{25}$

8) $\frac{96}{240} = \frac{2}{5}$

9) $\frac{36}{207} = \frac{4}{23}$

10) $\frac{21}{27} = \frac{7}{9}$

11) $\frac{440}{480} = \frac{11}{12}$

12) $\frac{420}{48} = 8\frac{3}{4}$

13) $\frac{6680}{800} = 8\frac{7}{20}$

14) $\frac{91}{140} = \frac{13}{20}$

15) $\frac{150}{30} = 5$

16) $\frac{486}{54} = 9$

17) $\frac{133}{21} = 6\frac{1}{3}$

18) $\frac{28}{60} = \frac{7}{15}$

19) $\frac{117}{360} = \frac{13}{40}$

20) $\frac{90}{144} = \frac{5}{8}$

21) $\frac{232}{240} = \frac{29}{30}$

22) $\frac{567}{135} = 4\frac{1}{5}$

23) $\frac{112}{56} = 2$

24) $\frac{9}{36} = \frac{1}{4}$

25) $\frac{600}{150} = 4$

26) $\frac{300}{100} = 3$

27) $\frac{128}{144} = \frac{8}{9}$

28) $\frac{24}{48} = \frac{1}{2}$

29) $\frac{1392}{150} = 9\frac{7}{25}$

30) $\frac{200}{375} = \frac{8}{15}$

31) $\frac{610}{105} = 5\frac{17}{21}$

32) $\frac{16}{40} = \frac{2}{5}$

Made in United States
North Haven, CT
16 April 2024